Non-League Football Supporters' Guide & Yearbook 2020

EDITOR
Steve Askew

Twenty-eighth Edition

For details of our range of over 2,300 books and around 300 DVDs, visit our web site or contact us using the information shown below.

British Library Cataloguing in Publication Data
A catalogue record for this book is available from the British Library

ISBN: 978-1-86223-407-9

Manufactured in the UK by Severn.

FOREWORD

Our thanks go to the numerous club officials who have aided us in the compilation of information contained in this guide as well as Michael Robinson (page layouts), Bob Budd (cover artwork) and Tony Brown (Cup Statistics – www.soccerdata.com).

Any readers who have up-to-date ground photographs which they would like us to consider for use in a future edition of this guide are requested to contact us at our address which is shown on the facing page.

The fixtures listed later in this book were released just a short time before we went to print and, as such, some of the dates shown may be subject to change. We therefore suggest that readers treat these fixtures as a rough guide and check dates carefully before attending matches.

We would like to wish our readers a safe and happy spectating season.

Steve Askew
EDITOR

CONTENTS

THE VANARAMA NATIONAL LEAGUE

Address   4th Floor, 20 Waterloo Street, Birmingham   B2 5TB

Phone (0121) 643-3143

Web site   www.footballconference.co.uk

Clubs for the 2019/2020 Season

AFC FYLDE

Photo courtesy of John Mills @ Altius Photography

Founded: 1988
Former Names: Formed by the amalgamation of Wesham FC and Kirkham Town FC in 1988
Nickname: 'The Coasters'
Ground: Mill Farm, Coronation Way, Wesham, Preston   PR4 3JZ
Record Attendance: 3,858 (26th December 2016)

Colours: White shirts and shorts
Telephone Nº: (01772) 682593
Fax Number: (01772) 685893
Ground Capacity: 6,000
Seating Capacity: 2,000
Pitch Size: 110 × 72 yards
Web Site: www.afcfylde.co.uk
E-mail: info@afcfylde.co.uk

GENERAL INFORMATION

Car Parking: A limited number of spaces are available at the ground and there is an overflow parking facility nearby.
Coach Parking: At the ground
Nearest Railway Station: Kirkham & Wesham (1 mile)
Club Shop: At the ground
Opening Times: Monday to Saturday 10.00am to 5.00pm. Tuesday Matchdays 10.00am to 10.00pm and Saturday Matchdays 9.00am to 6.00pm
Telephone Nº: (01772) 682593 (Phone orders accepted)

GROUND INFORMATION

Away Supporters' Entrances & Sections:
South Terrace standing and Seating in Block A.

ADMISSION INFO (2019/2020 PRICES)

Adult Standing: £14.00
Adult Seating: £18.00
Ages 16 to 21 Standing: £8.00
Under-16s Seating: £10.00
Under-16s Standing: £6.00
Note: Discounted prices are available for members.
Programme Price: £3.00

DISABLED INFORMATION

Wheelchairs: Accommodated
Helpers: Admitted
Prices: Normal prices apply for the disabled. One helper is admitted free of charge with each paying disabled fan.
Disabled Toilets: Available
Contact: (01772) 682593   (Bookings are necessary)

Travelling Supporters' Information:
Routes: The Mill Farm Sports Village is situated by the side of the A585, just to the north of Wesham and less than a mile to the south of Junction 3 of the M55.

ALDERSHOT TOWN FC

Founded: 2013 (as a new company)
Former Names: Aldershot Town FC
Nickname: 'Shots'
Ground: Ebb Stadium, High Street, Aldershot, GU11 1TW
Record Attendance: 7,500 (18th November 2000)
Pitch Size: 117 × 76 yards

Colours: Red shirts with Blue Sleeves, Blue shorts
Telephone N°: (01252) 320211
Club Secretary: (01252) 320211– Bob Green
Ground Capacity: 7,100
Seating Capacity: 2,136
Web site: www.theshots.co.uk
E-mail: admin@theshots.co.uk

GENERAL INFORMATION

Car Parking: Parsons Barracks Car Park is adjacent
Coach Parking: Contact the club for information
Nearest Railway Station: Aldershot (5 mins. walk)
Nearest Bus Station: Aldershot (5 minutes walk)
Club Shop: At the ground
Opening Times: Weekdays 10.00am to 4.00pm, Saturday matchdays 10.00am to 2.45pm and 9.30am to 7.30pm on Tuesday matchdays.
Telephone N°: (01252) 320211

GROUND INFORMATION

Away Supporters' Entrances & Sections:
Accommodation in the East Bank Terrace, Bill Warren section (South Stand) – Redan Hill Turnstiles N° 11 and 12.

ADMISSION INFO (2019/2020 PRICES)

Adult Standing/Seating: £20.00
Ages 11 to 18 Standing: £5.00
Ages 11 to 18 Seating: £7.00
Note: Under-11s are admitted free with paying adults – a maximum of 2 children per adult.
Concessionary Standing: £14.00
Concessionary Seating: £16.00
Note: Military personnel are charged Concessionary prices
Programme Price: £3.00

DISABLED INFORMATION

Wheelchairs: Accommodated in both the North Stand and the away section
Helpers: Admitted
Prices: Concessionary prices for the disabled. Helpers free.
Disabled Toilets: Available
Contact: (01252) 320211 (Bookings are required)

Travelling Supporters' Information:
Routes: From the M3: Exit at Junction 4 and follow signs for Aldershot (A331). Leave the A331 at the A323 exit (Ash Road) and continue along into the High Street. The ground is just past the Railway Bridge on the right; From the A31: Continue along the A31 to the junction with the A331, then as above; From the A325 (Farnborough Road): Follow signs to the A323 then turn left into Wellington Avenue. The ground is just off the 2nd roundabout on the left – the floodlights are clearly visible.

BARNET FC

Founded: 1888
Former Names: Barnet Alston FC
Nickname: 'The Bees'
Ground: The Hive, Camrose Avenue, Edgware, HA8 6AG
Record Attendance: 5,539 (5th May 2018)
Pitch Size: 112 × 73 yards

Colours: Shirts and shorts are Black and Amber
Telephone Nº: (020) 8381-3800
Ticket Office: (020) 8381-3800
Ground Capacity: 6,500
Seating Capacity: 5,419
Web site: www.barnetfc.com
E-mail: tellus@barnetfc.com

GENERAL INFORMATION

Car Parking: 350 spaces available at the ground
Coach Parking: Available at the ground
Nearest Railway Station: Harrow & Wealdstone (2½ miles)
Nearest Tube Station: Canons Park (5 minutes walk)
Club Shop: At the ground
Opening Times: Daily from 8.00am to 11.00pm – the shop is open throughout The Hive opening hours.
Telephone Nº: (020) 8381-3800

GROUND INFORMATION

Away Supporters' Entrances & Sections:
North Terrace and North West corner

ADMISSION INFO (2019/2020 PRICES)

Adult Standing: £15.00
Adult Seating: £22.00
Concessionary Standing: £10.00
Concessionary Seating: £14.00
Under-17s Standing: £1.00
Under-17s Seating: £5.00
Programme Price: £3.00

FANS WITH DISABILITIES INFORMATION

Wheelchairs: 42 covered spaces in total for Home and Away fans in the East and West Stands
Helpers: One helper admitted per wheelchair
Prices: Normal prices for fans with disabilities. Helpers free
Disabled Toilets: Available
Contact: (020) 8381-3800 (Bookings are advisable)

Travelling Supporters' Information:
Routes: Exit the M1 at Junction 4 and take the Edgware Way/Watford Bypass (A41). Take the 3rd exit at the roundabout onto the A410 then the first exit at the next roundabout along the A5 (Stonegrove), continuing for approximately 1½ miles. Turn right into Camrose Avenue and The Hive is approximately two-thirds of a mile along this road.

BARROW AFC

Founded: 1901
Former Names: None
Nickname: 'Bluebirds'
Ground: Furness Building Society Stadium, Barrow-in-Furness, Cumbria   LA14 5UW
Record Attendance: 16,874 (1954)
Pitch Size: 110 × 75 yards

Colours: White shirts with Blue sleeves, Blue shorts
Telephone Nº: (01229) 666010
Ground Capacity: 5,045
Seating Capacity: 1,000
Web site: www.barrowafc.com
E-mail: office@barrowafc.com

GENERAL INFORMATION

Car Parking: Street Parking, Popular Side Car Park and Soccer Bar Car Park
Coach Parking: Adjacent to the ground
Nearest Railway Station: Barrow Central (½ mile)
Nearest Bus Station: ½ mile
Club Shop: At the ground
Opening Times: Monday to Friday 9.00am to 4.00pm and Saturday Home Matchdays 12.00pm to 2.55pm.
Telephone Nº: (01229) 666010

GROUND INFORMATION

Away Supporters' Entrances & Sections:
Holker Street End (uncovered terrace)

ADMISSION INFO (2019/2020 PRICES)

Adult Standing: £15.00
Adult Seating: £18.00
Concessionary Standing: £12.00
Concessionary Seating: £14.00
Under-21s Standing/Seating: £5.00
Under-16s Standing/Seating: £3.00
Note: Tickets are cheaper if purchased in advance online.

DISABLED INFORMATION

Wheelchairs: 6 spaces available in the Disabled Area
Helpers: Admitted
Prices: Normal prices apply
Disabled Toilets: Available
Contact: (01229) 666010   (Bookings are not necessary) – r.sutherland@barrowafc.com (Disability Liaison Officer)

Travelling Supporters' Information:
Routes: Exit the M6 at Junction 36 and take the A590 through Ulverston. Using the bypass, follow signs for Barrow. After approximately 5 miles, turn left into Wilkie Road and the ground is on the right.

BOREHAM WOOD FC

Founded: 1948
Former Names: Boreham Rovers FC and Royal Retournez FC
Nickname: 'The Wood'
Ground: Meadow Park, Broughinge Road, Borehamwood, Hertfordshire   WD6 5AL
Record Attendance: 4,030 (2001)
Pitch Size: 112 × 72 yards

Colours: White shirts and shorts
Telephone Nº: (0208) 953-5097
Fax Number: (0208) 207-7982
Ground Capacity: 5,000
Seating Capacity: 1,700
Web site: www.borehamwoodfootballclub.co.uk

GENERAL INFORMATION

Car Parking: At the ground or in Brook Road car park
Coach Parking: At the ground
Nearest Railway Station: Elstree & Borehamwood (1 mile)
Nearest Bus Station: Barnet
Club Shop: At the ground
Opening Times: 9.00am to 10.00pm Monday to Thursday; 9.00am to 6.00pm at weekends
Telephone Nº: (0208) 953-5097

GROUND INFORMATION

Away Supporters' Entrances & Sections:
Use the Away Gate in the West Stand for access to South Stand accommodation.

ADMISSION INFO (2019/2020 PRICES)

Adult Standing/Seating: £20.00
Under-16s Standing/Seating: £10.00
Under-12s Standing/Seating: £8.00
Senior Citizen Standing/Seating: £15.00
Note:: Tickets are £2.00 cheaper when purchased in advance online (£3.00 cheaper for Under-12s).

DISABLED INFORMATION

Wheelchairs: Accommodated in the West Stand
Helpers: Admitted
Prices: Normal prices are charged for the disabled. Helpers are admitted free of charge.
Disabled Toilets: Available
Contact: (0208) 953-5097   (Bookings are not necessary)

Travelling Supporters' Information:
Routes: Exit the M25 at Junction 23 and take the A1 South. After 2 miles, take the Borehamwood exit onto the dual carriageway and go over the flyover following signs for Borehamwood for 1 mile. Turn right at the Studio roundabout into Brook Road, then next right into Broughinge Road for the ground.

BROMLEY FC

Founded: 1892
Former Names: None
Nickname: 'Lillywhites' 'The Ravens'
Ground: The Stadium, Hayes Lane, Bromley, Kent, BR2 9EF
Record Attendance: 10,798 (24th September 1949)
Pitch Size: 112 × 72 yards

Colours: White shirts with Black shorts
Telephone N°: (020) 8460-5291
Fax Number: (020) 8313-3992
Ground Capacity: 5,000
Seating Capacity: 1,300
Web site: www.bromleyfc.tv
E-mail: info@bromleyfc.co.uk

GENERAL INFORMATION

Car Parking: 300 spaces available at the ground
Coach Parking: At the ground
Nearest Railway Station: Bromley South (1 mile)
Nearest Bus Station: High Street, Bromley
Club Shop: At the ground
Opening Times: Matchdays only
Telephone N°: (020) 8460-5291

GROUND INFORMATION

Away Supporters' Entrances & Sections:
No usual segregation

ADMISSION INFO (2019/2020 PRICES)

Adult Standing/Seating: £15.00 (£18.00)
Concessionary Standing/Seating: £10.00 (£12.00)
Under-16s/Student Standing/Seating: £5.00 (£10.00)
Note: Prices shown are for tickets purchased in advance. Tickets purchased just before the game are more expensive (prices shown above in brackets). Discounted prices are available on the matchday for online bookings before 1.30pm or 6.30pm for day and night matches respectively. Under-16s are admitted free of charge with a paying adult for advance purchases up to 1 hour before kick-off. A special £10.00 discounted price is available for Season Ticket holders of Premiership and Football League clubs.

DISABLED INFORMATION

Wheelchairs: Accommodated
Prices: Concessionary prices are charged for disabled fans. Helpers are admitted free of charge
Disabled Toilets: Available
Contact: (0181) 460-5291   (Bookings are necessary)

Travelling Supporters' Information:
Routes: Exit the M25 at Junction 4 and follow the A21 for Bromley and London for approximately 4 miles before forking left onto the A232 signposted for Croydon/Sutton. At the second set of traffic lights turn right into Baston Road (B265) and follow for approximately 2 miles as it becomes Hayes Street and then Hayes Lane. The ground is on the right just after a mini-roundabout.

CHESTERFIELD FC

Founded: 1866
Former Names: Chesterfield Municipal FC, Chesterfield Town FC
Nickname: 'Spireites' 'Blues'
Ground: Proact Stadium , 1866 Sheffield Road, Whittington Moor, Chesterfield   S41 8NZ
Ground Capacity: 10,300 (All seats)

Record Attendance: 30,968 (Saltergate – 7/4/1939)
Pitch Size: 112 × 71 yards
Colours: Blue shirts with White shorts
Telephone Nº: (01246) 269300
Fax Number: (01246) 556799
Web Site: www.chesterfield-fc.co.uk

GENERAL INFORMATION

Car Parking: Various Car Parks available nearby
Coach Parking: At the ground
Nearest Railway Station: Chesterfield (1¼ miles)
Nearest Bus Station: Chesterfield
Club Shop: At the ground
Opening Times: Friday 9.00am to 5.00pm and Saturday Matchdays 9.00am to 3.15pm
Telephone Nº: (01246) 209765

GROUND INFORMATION

Away Supporters' Entrances & Sections:
H. Lilleker North Stand Turnstiles

ADMISSION INFO (2019/2020 PRICES)

Adult Seating: £18.00 – £22.00
Ages 17 to 21 Seating: £11.00 – £15.00
Juvenile (Under-17s) Seating: £7.00
Concessionary Seating: £14.00 – £18.00
Under-7s Seating: £5.00 in the Family Stand
Programme Price: £3.00

FANS WITH DISABILITIES INFORMATION

Wheelchairs: Up to 100 spaces available around the ground
Note: Lifts are available in the East and West stands
Helpers: One helper admitted per fan with disabilities
Prices: Concessionary prices for fans with disabilities. One helper admitted free of charge with each fan.
Disabled Toilets: Available in all stands
Contact: (01246) 269300   (Bookings are advised)

Travelling Supporters' Information:
Routes: From the South: Exit the M1 at Junction 29 and follow the A617 for Chesterfield. At the roundabout, take the 4th exit and head north on the A61 Sheffield Road and the stadium is located in the Whittington Moor district next to the junction with the A619; From the East: Take the A619 to Chesterfield and the ground is situated next to the Tesco supermarket at the junction with the A61; From the North: Exit the M1 at Junction 30 and take the A619 to Chesterfield. Then as above.

CHORLEY FC

Founded: 1883
Former Names: None
Nickname: 'Magpies'
Ground: The Chorley Group Victory Park Stadium, Duke Street, Chorley,   PR7 3DU
Record Attendance: 9,679 (v Darwen 15/11/1932)
Pitch Size: 112 × 72 yards

Colours: Black & White striped shirts with Black shorts
Telephone Nº: (01257) 230007
Fax Number: (01257) 275662
Ground Capacity: 4,100
Seating Capacity: 980
Web site: www.chorleyfc.com

GENERAL INFORMATION
Car Parking: Pilling Lane (£3.00)
Coach Parking: At the ground
Nearest Railway Station: Chorley (¼ mile)
Nearest Bus Station: 15 minutes from the ground
Club Shop: At the ground
Opening Times: Weekdays 12.00pm to 2.00pm and Matchdays 12.00pm until kick-off.
Telephone Nº: (01257) 230007

GROUND INFORMATION
Away Supporters' Entrances & Sections:
Pilling Lane Stand entrances and accommodation

ADMISSION INFO (2019/2020 PRICES)
Adult Standing: £15.00
Adult Seating: £15.00
Concessionary Standing/Seating: £12.00
Student (Ages 18 to 22) Standing/Seating: £7.00
Under-18s Standing/Seating: £5.00
Under-12s Standing/Seating: £1.00
Programme Price: £2.50

DISABLED INFORMATION
Wheelchairs: Accommodated by prior arrangement
Helpers: Please contact the club for information
Prices: Please contact the club for information
Disabled Toilets: Available in the Social Club
Contact: (01257) 230007 (Bookings are not necessary)

Travelling Supporters' Information:
Routes: Exit the M61 at Junction 6 and follow the A6 to Chorley. Going past the Yarrow Bridge Hotel on Bolton Road, turn left at the 1st set of traffic lights into Pilling Lane. Take the 1st right into Ashby Street and the ground is the 2nd entrance on the left; Alternative Route: Exit the M6 at Junction 27 and follow signs to Chorley. Turn left at the lights and continue down the A49 for 2½ miles before turning right onto B5251. On entering Chorley, turn right into Duke Street 200 yards past The Plough.

DAGENHAM & REDBRIDGE FC

Founded: 1992
Former Names: Formed by the merger of Dagenham FC and Redbridge Forest FC
Nickname: 'The Daggers'
Ground: Chigwell Construction Stadium, Victoria Road, Dagenham   RM10 7XL
Record Attendance: 5,949 (vs Ipswich Town in 2002)
Pitch Size: 110 × 70 yards

Colours: White shirts with Red shorts
Telephone N°: (020) 8592-1549
Office Phone N°: (020) 8592-7194
Secretary's Phone N°: (020) 8592-1549
Fax Number: (020) 8593-7227
Ground Capacity: 6,078 **Seating Capacity**: 2,233
Web site: www.daggers.co.uk
E-mail: info@daggers.co.uk

GENERAL INFORMATION
Car Parking: Street parking only
Coach Parking: Street parking only
Nearest Railway Station: Dagenham East (5 mins. walk)
Nearest Bus Station: Romford
Club Shop: At the ground
Opening Times: Monday & Tuesday 12.00pm – 4.00pm; Thursday 12.00pm – 8.00pm; Friday 12.00pm – 6.00pm; Saturday matchdays 1.00pm – 3.00pm.
Closed on Wednesdays, Sundays and non-match Saturdays
Telephone N°: (020) 8592-7194

GROUND INFORMATION
Away Supporters' Entrances & Sections:
Pondfield Road entrances for West Stand accommodation

ADMISSION INFO (2019/2020 PRICES)
Adult Standing: £15.00
Adult Seating: £15.00 – £21.00
Concessionary Standing: £10.00
Concessionary Seating: £10.00 – £15.00
Under-16s Standing: £8.00 (Under-10s free of charge)
Under-16s Seating: £8.00 – £12.00
Under-10s Seating: £2.00 (Free in the Family Stand)

DISABLED INFORMATION
Wheelchairs: Accommodated in front of the new Stand and the Family Stand
Helpers: Admitted
Prices: £15.00 for the disabled. Free of charge for Helpers
Disabled Toilets: Available at the East and West ends of the ground and also in the Clubhouse
Contact: (020) 8592-7194 (Bookings are necessary)

Travelling Supporters' Information:
Routes: From the North & West: Take the M11 to its end and join the A406 South. At the large roundabout take the slip road on the left signposted A13 to Dagenham. As you approach Dagenham, stay in the left lane and follow signs for A1306 signposted Dagenham East. Turn left onto the A1112 at the 5th set of traffic lights by the McDonalds. Proceed along Ballards Road to The Bull roundabout and bear left. Victoria Road is 450 yards on the left after passing Dagenham East tube station; From the South & East: Follow signs for the A13 to Dagenham. Take the next slip road off signposted Elm Park & Dagenham East then turn right at the roundabout. Go straight on at the next roundabout and turn left onto A1306. After ½ mile you will see a McDonalds on the right. Get into the right hand filter lane and turn right onto A1112. Then as from the North & West.   **SatNav**: RM10 7XL

DOVER ATHLETIC FC

Founded: 1983
Former Names: None
Nickname: 'The Whites'
Ground: Crabble Athletic Ground, Lewisham Road, River, Dover CT17 0JB
Record Attendance: 7,000 (vs Folkestone in 1951)
Pitch Size: 111 × 73 yards

Colours: White shirts with Black shorts
Telephone Nº: (01304) 822373
Fax Number: (01304) 821383
Ground Capacity: 5,745
Seating Capacity: 1,500
Web site: www.doverathletic.com
E-mail: enquiries@doverathletic.com

GENERAL INFORMATION
Car Parking: Street parking
Coach Parking: Street parking
Nearest Railway Station: Kearsney (1 mile)
Nearest Bus Station: Pencester Road, Dover (1½ miles)
Club Shop: At the ground
Opening Times: Saturdays 9.00am to 12.00pm
Telephone Nº: (01304) 822373

GROUND INFORMATION
Away Supporters' Entrances & Sections:
Segregation only used when required

ADMISSION INFO (2019/2020 PRICES)
Adult Standing/Seating: £18.00
Senior Citizen Standing/Seating: £15.00
Under-18s Standing/Seating: £9.00
Under-11s Standing/Seating: Free of charge

DISABLED INFORMATION
Wheelchairs: Approximately 6 spaces are available in the Family Stand
Helpers: Admitted
Prices: Normal prices are applied for the disabled, helpers are admitted free of charge.
Disabled Toilets: Three available
Contact: (01304) 822373 (Bookings are not necessary)

Travelling Supporters' Information:
Routes: Take the A2 to the Whitfield roundabout and take the 4th exit. Travel down the hill to the mini-roundabout then turn left and follow the road for 1 mile to the traffic lights on the hill. Turn sharp right and pass under the railway bridge – the ground is on the left after 300 yards.

EASTLEIGH FC

Founded: 1946
Former Names: Swaythling Athletic FC and Swaythling FC
Nickname: 'The Spitfires'
Ground: The Silverlake Stadium, Stoneham Lane, Eastleigh   SO50 9HT
Record Attendance: 5,025 (2016)
Pitch Size: 112 × 74 yards

Colours: Blue shirts, shorts and socks
Telephone N°: (023) 8061-3361
Fax Number: (023) 8061-2379
Ground Capacity: 5,192
Seating Capacity: 3,210
Web site: www.eastleighfc.com
e-mail: admin@eastleighfc.com

GENERAL INFORMATION

Car Parking: Spaces for 450 cars (hard standing – £5.00)
Coach Parking: At the ground
Nearest Railway Station: Southampton Parkway (¾ mile)
Nearest Bus Station: Eastleigh (2 miles)
Club Shop: At the ground
Opening Times: Monday to Friday 10.00am to 4.00pm plus Saturday and Weekdays Matchdays 9.00am until kick-off, then for 30 minutes after the game.
Telephone N°: (023) 8061-3361

GROUND INFORMATION

Away Supporters' Entrances & Sections:
Mackay Community Stand, Blocks 1, 2 & 3 – entrance via Turnstiles 10 and 11

ADMISSION INFO (2019/2020 PRICES)

Adult Standing: £12.00   **Adult Seating**: £15.00
Concessionary Standing: £8.00
Concessionary Seating: £10.00
Under-18s Standing: £4.00   **Under-18s Seating**: £5.00
Under-7s Standing/Seating: Free of charge
Note: Discounted prices are available for advance purchases

DISABLED INFORMATION

Wheelchairs: Over 20 spaces available.
Helpers: Admitted
Prices: Normal prices for the disabled. Helpers free of charge
Disabled Toilets: Available
Contact: (023) 8061-3361   (Bookings are not necessary) – Sarah Woolley – dlo@eastleighfc.com

Travelling Supporters' Information:
Routes: Exit the M27 at Junction 5 (signposted for Southampton Airport) and take the A335 (Stoneham Way) towards Southampton. After ½ mile, turn right at the traffic lights into Bassett Green Road. Turn right at the next set of traffic lights into Stoneham Lane and the ground is on the right after ¾ mile.

EBBSFLEET UNITED FC

Founded: 1946
Former Names: Gravesend & Northfleet United FC, Gravesend United FC and Northfleet United FC
Nickname: 'The Fleet'
Ground: The Kuflink Stadium, Stonebridge Road, Northfleet, Gravesend, Kent   DA11 9GN
Record Attendance: 12,036 (vs Sunderland 1963)
Pitch Size: 112 × 72 yards

Colours: Reds shirts with White shorts
Telephone Nº: (01474) 533796
Fax Number: (01474) 324754
Ground Capacity: 4,769
Seating Capacity: 2,179
Web site: www.ebbsfleetunited.co.uk
E-mail: info@eufc.co.uk

GENERAL INFORMATION

Car Parking: Ebbsfleet International Car Park C (when available) and also street parking
Coach Parking: At the ground
Nearest Railway Station: Northfleet (5 minutes walk)
Nearest Bus Station: Bus Stop outside the ground
Club Shop: At the ground
Opening Times: Weekdays 9.00am to 5.00pm
Telephone Nº: (01474) 533796

GROUND INFORMATION

Away Supporters' Entrances & Sections:
Only certain games are segregated, when the Swanscombe End turnstiles are allocated to away supporters.
Please contact the club for further details

ADMISSION INFO (2019/2020 PRICES)

Adult Standing: £17.00
Adult Seating: £17.00
Over-60s/Student Standing: £14.00
Under-17s Standing/Seating: £9.00
Under-12s Standing/Seating: £1.00 when accompanied by a paying adult (maximum of 2 per adult).

DISABLED INFORMATION

Wheelchairs: 6 spaces are available in the Disabled Area in front of the Main Stand
Helpers: Admitted free of charge
Prices: Normal prices apply for disabled fans
Disabled Toilets: Available in the Main Stand
Contact: (01474) 533796   (Bookings are necessary) – Cheryl Wanless – cheryl@eufc.co.uk (Disability Liaison Officer)

Travelling Supporters' Information:
Routes: Take the A2 to the Northfleet/Southfleet exit and follow signs for Northfleet (B262). Go straight on at the first roundabout then take the 2nd exit at the 2nd roundabout into Thames Way and follow the football signs for the ground.

FC HALIFAX TOWN

Founded: 1911 (Re-formed 2008)
Former Names: Halifax Town FC
Nickname: 'The Shaymen'
Ground: The MBi Shay Stadium, Shay Syke, Halifax, HX1 2YT
Ground Capacity: 10,568
Seating Capacity: 5,285

Record Attendance: 8,042 (vs Bradford City, 2014)
Pitch Size: 112 × 73 yards
Colours: Blue shirts and shorts
Telephone Nº: (01422) 341222
Fax Number: (01422) 349487
Web Site: www.fchalifaxtown.co.uk

GENERAL INFORMATION
Car Parking: Adjacent to the East Stand and also Shaw Hill Car Park (Nearby)
Coach Parking: By arrangement with the Club Secretary
Nearest Railway Station: Halifax (10 minutes walk)
Nearest Bus Station: Halifax (15 minutes walk)
Club Shop: At the ground in the East Stand
Opening Times: Please phone for details
Telephone Nº: (01422) 341222

GROUND INFORMATION
Away Supporters' Entrances & Sections:
Skircoat Stand (Seating only)

ADMISSION INFO (2019/2020 PRICES)
Adult Standing/Seating: £20.00
Senior Citizen Standing/Seating: £17.00
Under-12s Standing/Seating: £5.00
Under-7s Standing/Seating: £3.00

DISABLED INFORMATION
Wheelchairs: 33 spaces available in total in disabled sections in the East Stand and South Stand
Helpers: One admitted free with each paying disabled fan
Prices: Free of charge for the disabled and helpers
Disabled Toilets: Available in the East and South Stands
Contact: (01422) 341222 (Bookings are not necessary)

Travelling Supporters' Information:
Routes: From the North: Take the A629 to Halifax Town Centre. Take the 2nd exit at the roundabout into Broad Street and follow signs for Huddersfield (A629) into Skircoat Road; From the South, East and West: Exit the M62 at Junction 24 and follow Halifax (A629) signs for the Town Centre into Skircoat Road then Shaw Hill for ground.   **SatNav**: Use HX1 2YS for the ground.

HARROGATE TOWN AFC

Founded: 1919
Former Names: Harrogate FC and Harrogate Hotspurs FC
Nickname: 'Town'
Ground: CNG Stadium, Wetherby Road, Harrogate, HG2 7SA
Record Attendance: 15,000 (vs Sheffield Utd, 1920)
Pitch Size: 107 × 72 yards

Colours: Yellow and Black striped shirts, Black shorts
Telephone Nº: (01423) 210600
Ground Capacity: 4,200
Seating Capacity: 648
Web site: www.harrogatetownafc.com
E-mail: enquiries@harrogatetownafc.com

GENERAL INFORMATION

Car Parking: Hospital Car Park adjacent
Coach Parking: At the ground
Nearest Railway Station: Harrogate (¾ mile)
Nearest Bus Station: Harrogate
Club Shop: At the ground
Opening Times: Monday to Friday 9.00am to 3.00pm and also on Matchdays
Telephone Nº: (01423) 210600

GROUND INFORMATION

Away Supporters' Entrances & Sections:
No usual segregation

ADMISSION INFO (2019/2020 PRICES)

Adult Standing: £18.00
Adult Seating: £19.00
Concessionary Standing: £14.00
Concessionary Seating: £15.00
Under-18s Standing: £8.00
Under-18s Seating: £9.00

DISABLED INFORMATION

Wheelchairs: Accommodated at the front of the Main Stand
Helpers: One helper admitted for each disabled fan
Prices: Free of charge for each disabled fan and helper
Disabled Toilets: Available
Contact: (01423) 210600 (Bookings are necessary)

Travelling Supporters' Information:
Routes: From the South: Take the A61 from Leeds and turn right at the roundabout onto the ring road (signposted York). After about 1¼ miles turn left at the next roundabout onto A661 Wetherby Road. The ground is situated ¾ mile on the right; From the West: Take the A59 straight into Wetherby Road from Empress Roundabout and the ground is on the left; From the East & North: Exit the A1(M) at Junction 47, take the A59 to Harrogate then follow the Southern bypass to Wetherby Road for the A661 Roundabout. Turn right towards Harrogate Town Centre and the ground is on the right after ¾ mile.

HARTLEPOOL UNITED FC

Founded: 1908
Former Names: Hartlepools United FC (1908-68); Hartlepool FC (1968-77)
Nickname: 'The Pool' 'Pools'
Ground: The Super 6 Stadium, Clarence Road, Hartlepool   TS24 8BZ
Ground Capacity: 7,865   **Seating Capacity**: 4,359
Record Attendance: 17,426 (15th January 1957)

Pitch Size: 110 × 74 yards
Colours: Blue and White striped shirts with Blue shorts
Telephone N°: (01429) 272584
Ticket Office: (01429) 272584 Option 2
Ticket Office e-mail: tickets@hartlepoolunited.co.uk
Fax Number: (01429) 863007
Web Site: www.hartlepoolunited.co.uk
E-mail: enquiries@hartlepoolunited.co.uk

GENERAL INFORMATION

Car Parking: Limited space at the ground (£5.00 charge) and also street parking
Coach Parking: Church Street
Nearest Railway Station: Hartlepool Church Street (5 minutes walk)
Club Shop: At the ground
Opening Times: Tuesday, Thursday and Friday 10.00am to 4.00pm and Saturday Matchdays 10.00am to 3.00pm.
Telephone N°: (01429) 260491

GROUND INFORMATION

Away Supporters' Entrances & Sections:
Clarence Road turnstiles 1 & 2 for Smith & Graham Stand

ADMISSION INFO (2019/2020 PRICES)

Adult Standing: £18.00
Adult Seating: £20.00
Senior Citizen/Under-19s/Student Standing: £9.00
Senior Citizen/Under-19s/Student Seating: £10.00
Under-16s: Admitted for £5.00 with a paying adult
Programme Price: £3.00

DISABLED INFORMATION

Wheelchairs: 21 spaces for Home fans in disabled section, Camerons CK Stand, 10 spaces for Away fans in the Smith & Graham Stand.
Helpers: One helper admitted per wheelchair
Prices: £20.00 for the Disabled. Helpers free of charge
Disabled Toilets: Available in the Camerons CK Stand
Contact: (01429) 272584 Option 9 (Bookings advisable)

Travelling Supporters' Information: **Routes**: From the North: Take the A1/A19 to the A179 and follow Town Centre/ Marina signs. Turn right at the roundabout by the 'Historic Quayside' and cross over the Railway bridge. The ground is on the left; From the South & West: Take the A689 following Town Centre/Marina signs. Turn left at the roundabout by the 'Historic Quayside' and cross over the Railway bridge. The ground is on the left.

MAIDENHEAD UNITED FC

Founded: 1870
Former Names: None
Nickname: 'Magpies'
Ground: York Road, Maidenhead, Berks. SL6 1SF
Record Attendance: 7,920 (vs Southall in 1936)
Pitch Size: 110 × 75 yards

Colours: Black and White striped shirts, Black shorts
Telephone Nº: (01628) 636314 (Club)
Ground Capacity: 4,000
Seating Capacity: 550
Web: www.pitchero.com/clubs/maidenheadunited
E-mail: social@maidenheadunitedfc.org

GENERAL INFORMATION
Car Parking: Street parking
Coach Parking: Street parking
Nearest Railway Station: Maidenhead (¼ mile)
Nearest Bus Station: Maidenhead
Club Shop: At the ground
Opening Times: Matchdays only
Telephone Nº: (01628) 624739

GROUND INFORMATION
Away Supporters' Entrances & Sections:
No usual segregation

ADMISSION INFO (2019/2020 PRICES)
Adult Standing: £15.00
Adult Seating: £15.00
Concessionary Standing and Seating: £10.00
Under-16s Standing and Seating: £5.00
Note: Junior Magpies (Under-16s) are admitted free to
matches in the League.
Programme Price: £2.00

DISABLED INFORMATION
Wheelchairs: Accommodated
Helpers: Admitted
Prices: Normal prices for the disabled. Free for helpers
Disabled Toilets: Available
Contact: (01628) 636314 (Bookings are not necessary)

Travelling Supporters' Information:
Routes: Exit M4 at Junction 7 and take the A4 to Maidenhead. Cross the River Thames bridge and turn left at the 2nd roundabout passing through the traffic lights. York Road is first right and the ground is approximately 300 yards along on the left.

NOTTS COUNTY FC

Founded: 1862 (**Entered League**: 1888)
Nickname: 'The Magpies'
Ground: Meadow Lane Stadium, Nottingham, NG2 3HJ
Ground Capacity: 19,841 (All seats)
Record Attendance: 47,310 (12th March 1955)
Pitch Size: 109 × 72 yards

Colours: Black and White striped shirts, Black shorts
Telephone Nº: (0115) 952-9000
Ticket Office: (0115) 955-7210
Web Site: www.nottscountyfc.co.uk
E-mail: office@nottscountyfc.co.uk

GENERAL INFORMATION

Car Parking: Meadow Lane and Cattle Market
Coach Parking: Incinerator Road (Cattle Market Corner)
Nearest Railway Station: Nottingham (½ mile)
Nearest Bus Station: Broadmarsh Centre (Station Street)
Club Shop: At the ground
Opening Times: Mondays to Friday 9.00am – 5.00pm, Saturday Matchdays 9.00am – 5.30pm, other Saturdays 9.00am – 1.00pm
Telephone Nº: (0115) 955-7200

GROUND INFORMATION

Away Supporters' Entrances & Sections:
Jimmy Sirrel Stand, Block Z – use Turnstiles 19-24

ADMISSION INFO (2019/2020 PRICES)

Adult Seating: £22.00
Under-18s Seating: £9.00
Ages 18 to 21 Seating: £16.00
Senior Citizen Seating: £16.00
Under-16s Seating: £7.00
Under-12s Seating: £1.00   (Under-7s admitted free)
Note: Discounted prices are available for advance purchases
Programme Price: £3.00

DISABLED INFORMATION

Wheelchairs: 34 spaces for home fans in the Derek Pavis Stand and Haydn Green Family Stand and 10 spaces for away fans in the Jimmy Sirrel Stand
Helpers: One helper admitted with each disabled fan
Prices: Normal prices apply for fans with disabilities.
Disabled Toilets: Available
Contact: (0115) 955-7241   (Bookings are necessary)

Travelling Supporters' Information:
Routes: From the North: Exit the M1 at Junction 26 following Nottingham signs (A610) then Melton Mowbray and Trent Bridge (A606) signs. Before the River Trent turn left into Meadow Lane; From the South: Exit the M1 at Junction 24 following signs for Nottingham (South) to Trent Bridge, cross the river and follow the one-way system to the right, then turn left and right at the traffic lights then second right into Meadow Lane; From the East: Take the A52 to West Bridgford/Trent Bridge, cross the river and follow the one-way system to the right then turn left and right at the traffic lights, then second right into Meadow Lane; From the West: Take the A52 into Nottingham following signs for Melton Mowbray and Trent Bridge. Before the River Trent turn left into Meadow Lane.

SOLIHULL MOORS FC

Photo courtesy of Jordan Martin Photography

Founded: 2007
Former Names: Formed by the merger of Solihull Borough FC and Moor Green FC in 2007
Nickname: 'The Moors'
Ground: The Autotmated Technology Group Stadium, Damson Parkway, Solihull   B91   2PP
Record Attendance: 3,681   (vs AFC Fylde, 2019)
Pitch Size: 114 × 76 yards

Colours: Yellow and Blue shirts with Blue shorts
Telephone Nº: (0121) 705-6770
Fax Number: (0121) 711-4045
Ground Capacity: 4,161   (Subject to change
Seating Capacity: 2,522   following redevelopment)
Web site: www.solihullmoorsfc.co.uk
E-mail: info@solihullmoorsfc.co.uk

GENERAL INFORMATION

Car Parking: Limited number of spaces at the ground (£5.00 charge per car)
Coach Parking: At the ground
Nearest Railway Station: Birmingham International (2 miles)
Nearest Bus Station: Birmingham (5 miles)
Club Shop: At the ground
Opening Times: Matchdays only
Telephone Nº: (0121) 705-6770

GROUND INFORMATION

Away Supporters' Entrances & Sections:
No usual segregation

ADMISSION INFO (2019/2020 PRICES)

Adult Standing: £16.00   (Online £15.00)
Adult Seating: £18.00   (Online £17.00)
Senior Citizen/Junior Standing: £9.00   (Online £8.00)
Senior Citizen/Junior Seating: £12.00   (Online £11.00)
Note: Under-12s are admitted free of charge when accompanied by a paying adult. Tickets are cheaper if purchased in advance online.

DISABLED INFORMATION

Wheelchairs: Spaces for 3 wheelchairs are available
Helpers: Admitted
Prices: Normal prices for fans with disabilities. Helpers free
Disabled Toilets: Available
Contact: (0121) 705-6770

Travelling Supporters' Information:
Routes: Exit the M42 at Junction 6 and take the A45 for 2 miles towards Birmingham. Turn left at the traffic lights near the Posthouse Hotel into Damson Parkway (signposted for Landrover/Damsonwood). Continue to the roundabout and come back along the other carriageway to the ground which is situated on the left after about 150 yards.

STOCKPORT COUNTY FC

Photohraph courtesy of Mike Petch – Mphotographic.co.uk

Founded: 1883
Former Names: Heaton Norris Rovers FC
Nickname: 'Hatters' 'County'
Ground: Edgeley Park, Hardcastle Road, Edgeley, Stockport   SK3 9DD
Ground Capacity: 10,841 (All seats)
Record Attendance: 27,833 (11th February 1950)
Pitch Size: 111 × 72 yards

Colours: Blue shirts and shorts
Telephone Nº: (0161) 266-2700
Ticket Office: (0161) 266-2700
Ticket Office E-mail: tickets@stockportcounty.com
Web Site: www.stockportcounty.com
E-mail: info@stockportcounty.com
or mark.lockyear@stockportcounty.com

GENERAL INFORMATION

Car Parking: Available at the end of Castle Street in Edgeley
Coach Parking: As above
Nearest Railway Station: Stockport (5 minutes walk)
Nearest Bus Station: Mersey Square (10 minutes walk)
Club Shop: At the ground
Opening Times: Wednesday to Friday 12.00pm–4.00pm. Open until 7.45pm on matchdays during the week and also on Saturday matchdays 10.00am – 3.00pm then for 30 minutes after the game.
Telephone Nº: (0161) 266-2700

GROUND INFORMATION

Away Supporters' Entrances & Sections:
Railway End turnstiles for Railway End or turnstiles for Popular Side depending on the opponents

ADMISSION INFO (2019/2020 PRICES)

Adult Seating: £18.00
Senior Citizen/Student Seating: £12.00
Under-18s Seating: £5.00
Note: Children under the age of 6 are admitted free.

DISABLED INFORMATION

Wheelchairs: 16 spaces in total. 10 in the Hardcastle Road Stand, 6 in the Cheadle Stand
Helpers: One helper admitted per disabled fan
Prices: £12.00 for the disabled. Helpers free of charge
Disabled Toilets: Available
Contact: (0161) 266-2700   (Bookings are necessary)

Travelling Supporters' Information:
Routes: From the North, South and West: Exit the M60 at Junction 1 and join the A560, following signs for Cheadle. After ¼ mile turn right into Edgeley Road and after 1 mile turn right into Caroline Street for the ground; From the East: Take the A6 or A560 into Stockport Town Centre and turn left into Greek Street. Take the 2nd exit into Mercian Way (from the roundabout) then turn left into Caroline Street – the ground is straight ahead.

SUTTON UNITED FC

Founded: 1898
Former Names: Formed by the amalgamation of Sutton Guild Rovers FC and Sutton Association FC
Nickname: 'U's'
Ground: The Knights Community Stadium, Sutton Sports Ground, Gander Green Lane, Sutton SM1 2EY
Record Attendance: 14,000 (vs Leeds United, 1970)

Colours: Amber shirts and shorts
Telephone Nº: (020) 8644-4440
Fax Number: (020) 8644-5120
Ground Capacity: 5,013
Seating Capacity: 765
Web site: www.suttonunited.net
E-mail: info@suttonunited.net

GENERAL INFORMATION

Car Parking: 150 spaces behind the Main Stand for permit holders only. Otherwise, street parking is usually possible
Coach Parking: Space for 1 coach in the car park
Nearest Railway Station: West Sutton (adjacent)
Club Shop: At the ground
Opening Times: Matchdays only
Telephone Nº: (020) 8644-4440

GROUND INFORMATION

Away Supporters' Entrances & Sections:
Collingwood Road entrances and accommodation

ADMISSION INFO (2019/2020 PRICES)

Adult Standing: £17.00
Adult Seating: £20.00
Under-18s Standing: £5.00
Under-18s Seating: £8.00
Concessionary Standing: £10.00
Concessionary Seating: £13.00
Note: Under-11s are admitted free of charge

DISABLED INFORMATION

Wheelchairs: 8 spaces are available under cover accommodated on the track perimeter
Helpers: Admitted
Prices: Normal prices apply for the disabled. Free for helpers
Disabled Toilets: Available alongside the Standing Terrace
Contact: (020) 8644-4440 (Bookings are necessary)

Travelling Supporters' Information:
Routes: Exit the M25 at Junction 8 (Reigate Hill) and travel North on the A217 for approximately 8 miles. Cross the A232 then turn right at the traffic lights (past Goose & Granit Public House) into Gander Green Lane. The ground is 300 yards on the left; From London: Gander Green Lane crosses the Sutton bypass 1 mile south of Rose Hill Roundabout. Avoid Sutton Town Centre, especially on Saturdays.

TORQUAY UNITED FC

Founded: 1899
Former Name: Torquay Town FC (1899-1910)
Nickname: 'Gulls'
Ground: Plainmoor Ground, Torquay   TQ1 3PS
Ground Capacity: 6,200   **Seating Capacity**: 2,841
Record Attendance: 21,908 (29th January 1955)
Pitch Size: 112 × 72 yards

Colours: Yellow shirts and Blue shorts
Telephone Nº: (01803) 328666
Ticket Office: (01803) 328666
Fax Number: (01803) 323976
Web Site: www.torquayunited.com
E-mail: reception@torquayunited.com

GENERAL INFORMATION
Car Parking: Street parking
Coach Parking: Lymington Road Coach Station (½ mile)
Nearest Railway Station: Torquay (2 miles)
Nearest Bus Station: Lymington Road (½ mile)
Club Shop: At the ground
Opening Times: Monday to Friday 10.00am to 4.30pm, Tuesday Matchdays 10.00am until kick-off then until after the final whistle until 10.00pm. Saturday Matchdays 12.00pm to 3.00pm then until 5.30pm following the final whistle.
Telephone Nº: (01803) 328666

GROUND INFORMATION
Away Supporters' Entrances & Sections:
Riviera Rentals away terrace

ADMISSION INFO (2019/2020 PRICES)
Adult Standing: £15.00
Adult Seating: £16.00 – £17.00
Concessionary Standing: £13.00
Concessionary Seating: £14.00 – £15.00
Under-18s Standing/Seating: £9.00
Note: Under-7s are admitted free with a paying adult and Family tickets are also available.
Programme Price: £3.00

DISABLED INFORMATION
Wheelchairs: Spaces for both Home and Away fans are available in front of Bristow Bench Stand.
Helpers: One helper admitted per wheelchair
Prices: Normal prices for the disabled. Free for helpers
Disabled Toilets: In the Ellacombe End and the Away End
Contact: (01803) 328666   (Bookings are not necessary)

Travelling Supporters' Information:
Routes: From the North and East: Take the M5 to the A38 then A380 to Torquay. On entering Torquay, turn left at the 1st set of traffic lights after Riviera Way Retail Park into Hele Road. Following signs for the ground, continue straight on over two mini-roundabouts, go up West Hill Road to the traffic lights, then straight ahead into Warbro Road. The ground is situated on the right after 200 yards.

WOKING FC

Founded: 1889
Former Names: None
Nickname: 'Cardinals'
Ground: Laithwaite Community Stadium, Kingfield, Woking, Surrey   GU22 9AA
Record Attendance: 6,064 (vs Coventry City, 1997)
Pitch Size: 109 × 76 yards

Colours: Shirts are Red & White halves, Black shorts
Telephone Nº: (01483) 772470
Fax Number: (01483) 888423
Ground Capacity: 6,161
Seating Capacity: 2,511
Web site: www.wokingfc.co.uk
E-mail: admin@wokingfc.co.uk

GENERAL INFORMATION

Car Parking: Limited parking at the ground
Coach Parking: Please contact the club for details
Nearest Railway Station: Woking (1 mile)
Nearest Bus Station: Woking
Club Shop: At the ground
Opening Times: Weekdays 10.15am to 2.45pm (3.45pm on Wednesdays). Saturday Matchdays 1.00pm to 3.00pm.
Telephone Nº: (01483) 772470 Extension 240

GROUND INFORMATION

Away Supporters' Entrances & Sections:
Kingfield Road entrance for the Chris Lane terrace

ADMISSION INFO (2019/2020 PRICES)

Adult Standing: £18.00
Adult Seating: £18.00
Under-16s/Student Standing: £5.00
Under-16s/Student Seating: £5.00
Senior Citizen Standing: £13.00
Senior Citizen Seating: £13.00

DISABLED INFORMATION

Wheelchairs: 8 spaces in the Leslie Gosden Stand and 8 spaces in front of the Family Stand
Helpers: Admitted
Prices: Concessionary prices apply for disabled fans. Helpers are admitted free of charfge
Disabled Toilets: Yes – in the Leslie Gosden Stand and Family Stand area
Contact: (01483) 772470 (Bookings are necessary)

Travelling Supporters' Information:
Routes: Exit the M25 at Junction 10 and follow the A3 towards Guildford. Leave at the next junction onto the B2215 through Ripley and join the A247 to Woking. Alternatively, exit the M25 at Junction 11 and follow the A320 to Woking Town Centre. The ground is on the outskirts of Woking – follow signs on the A320 and A247.

WREXHAM AFC

Founded: 1864
Nickname: 'Red Dragons'
Ground: Racecourse Ground, Mold Road, Wrexham, North Wales   LL11 2AH
Ground Capacity: 10,500 (all seats)
Record Attendance: 34,445 (26th January 1957)
Pitch Size: 111 × 68 yards

Colours: Red shirts with White shorts
Telephone Nº: (01978) 891864
Web Site: www.wrexhamafc.co.uk
E-mail: info@wrexhamfc.tv

GENERAL INFORMATION

Car Parking: Town car parks are nearby and also Glyndwr University (Mold End)
Coach Parking: By Police direction
Nearest Railway Station: Wrexham General (adjacent)
Nearest Bus Station: Wrexham (King Street)
Club Shop: At the ground under the bkoncepts Stand
Opening Times: Monday to Friday 10.00am to 5.00pm
Telephone Nº: (01978) 891864

GROUND INFORMATION

Away Supporters' Entrances & Sections:
Turnstiles 1-4 for the bkoncepts Stand

ADMISSION INFO (2019/2020 PRICES)

Adult Seating: £16.00 – £20.00
Concession Seniors/Under-21s Seating: £13.00–£15.00
Concession Over-80s/Under-18s Seating: £7.00 – £8.00
Under-11s Seating: £1.00 (with a paying adult)
Note: Discounts apply for advance purchases and Family tickets are also available

DISABLED INFORMATION

Wheelchairs: 35 spaces in the Mold Road Stand
Helpers: One helper admitted per wheelchair
Prices: Normal prices for the disabled. Free for helpers
Disabled Toilets: Available in the disabled section
Contact: (01978) 891864

Travelling Supporters' Information:
Routes: From the North and West: Take the A483 and the Wrexham bypass to the junction with the A541. Branch left at the roundabout and follow Wrexham signs into Mold Road; From the East: Take the A525 or A534 into Wrexham then follow the A541 signs into Mold Road; From the South: Take the the M6, then the M54 and follow the A5 and A483 to the Wrexham bypass and the junction with the A541. Branch right at the roundabout and follow signs for the Town Centre.

YEOVIL TOWN FC

Founded: 1895
Former Names: Yeovil & Petters United FC
Nickname: 'Glovers'
Ground: Huish Park Stadium, Lufton Way, Yeovil, Somerset BA22 8YF
Ground Capacity: 9,565 **Seating Capacity**: 5,309
Record Attendance: 9,527 (25th April 2008)

Pitch Size: 108 × 67 yards
Colours: Green and White shirts with White shorts
Telephone N°: (01935) 423662
Ticket Office N°: (01935) 847888
Fax Number: (01935) 473956
Web site: www.ytfc.net
E-mail: info@ytfc.net

GENERAL INFORMATION

Car Parking: Spaces for 800 cars at the ground (£3.00)
Coach Parking: At the ground
Nearest Railway Station: Yeovil Pen Mill (2½ miles) and Yeovil Junction (3½ miles)
Nearest Bus Station: Yeovil (2 miles)
Club Shop: At the ground
Opening Times: Weekdays 10.00am – 4.00pm and Matchdays 10.00am – 3.00pm
Telephone N°: (01935) 423662

GROUND INFORMATION

Away Supporters' Entrances & Sections:
Away Terrace (turnstiles 13-16) and Screwfix Community Stand (turnstile 12)

ADMISSION INFO (2019/2020 PRICES)

Adult Standing: £16.00
Adult Seating: £19.00
Under-16s Standing/Seating: £3.00
Ages 16 to 22 Standing/Seating: £12.00
Senior Citizen/Armed Forces Standing: £14.00
Senior Citizen/Armed Forces Seating: £17.00
Note: Discounted prices are available for tickets which are purchased before the day of the match.

DISABLED INFORMATION

Wheelchairs: 15 spaces for home fans, 5 spaces for away fans
Helpers: Admitted free of charge
Prices: Concessionary prices apply for disabled fans
Disabled Toilets: Two are available
Contact: (01935) 847888 (Bookings are recommended)

Travelling Supporters' Information:
Routes: From London: Take the M3 and A303 to Cartgate Roundabout. Enter Yeovil on the A3088. Exit left at the 1st roundabout then straight over the next two roundabouts into Western Avenue. Cross the next roundabout then turn left into Copse Road, where supporters' parking is sited; From the North: Exit the M5 at Junction 25 and take the A358 (Ilminster) and A303 (Eastbound) entering Yeovil on the A3088. Then as above.

THE VANARAMA NATIONAL LEAGUE NORTH

Address

4th Floor, 20 Waterloo Street,
Birmingham   B2 5TB

Phone (0121) 643-3143

Web site www.footballconference.co.uk

Clubs for the 2019/2020 Season

AFC TELFORD UNITED

Founded: 2004
Former Names: Formed after Telford United FC went out of business. TUFC were previously known as Wellington Town FC
Nickname: 'The Bucks'
Ground: The New Bucks Head Stadium, Watling Street, Wellington, Telford TF1 2TU
Record Attendance: 13,000 (1935)

Pitch Size: 110 × 74 yards
Colours: White shirts with Black shorts
Telehone Nº: (01952) 640064
Fax Number: (01952) 640021
Ground Capacity: 6,300
Seating Capacity: 2,200
Web site: www.telfordunited.com
E-mail: enquiries@afctu.co.uk

GENERAL INFORMATION

Car Parking: At the ground (£3.00 charge for cars)
Coach Parking: At the ground
Nearest Railway Station: Wellington
Nearest Bus Station: Wellington
Club Shop: At the ground
Opening Times: Saturday matchdays only from 1.30pm.
Telephone Nº: (01952) 640064

GROUND INFORMATION

Away Supporters' Entrances & Sections:
Frank Nagington Stand on the rare occasions when segregation is used

ADMISSION INFO (2019/2020 PRICES)

Adult Standing: £14.00
Adult Seating: £14.00
Under-16s Standing: £1.00
Under-16s Seating: £1.00
Under-20s Standing: £5.00
Under-20s Seating: £5.00
Concessionary Standing: £8.00
Concessionary Seating: £8.00

DISABLED INFORMATION

Wheelchairs: Accommodated at both ends of the ground
Helpers: Admitted
Prices: Concessionary prices apply for disabled supporters. Helpers are admitted free of charge
Disabled Toilets: Available by the Sir Stephen Roberts Stand
Contact: (01952) 640064   (Bookings are not necessary)

Travelling Supporters' Information:
Routes: Exit the M54 at Junction 6 and take the A518. Go straight on at the first roundabout, take the second exit at the next roundabout then turn left at the following roundabout. Follow the road round to the right then turn left into the car park.

ALFRETON TOWN FC

Founded: 1959
Former Names: None
Nickname: 'Reds'
Ground: The Impact Arena, North Street, Alfreton, Derbyshire   DE55 7FZ
Record Attendance: 5,023 vs Matlock Town (1960)
Pitch Size: 110 × 75 yards

Colours: Red shirts and shorts
Telephone Nº: (01773) 830277
Ground Capacity: 4,000
Seating Capacity: 1,600
Web site: www.alfretontownfc.com
E-mail: enquiries@alfretontownfc.com

GENERAL INFORMATION

Car Parking: At the ground
Coach Parking: Available close to the ground
Nearest Railway Station: Alfreton (½ mile)
Nearest Bus Station: Alfreton (5 minutes walk)
Club Shop: At the ground
Opening Times: Weekdays 9.00am to 3.00pm
Telephone Nº: (01773) 830277

GROUND INFORMATION

Away Supporters' Entrances & Sections:
Segregation is usual so please check prior to the game

ADMISSION INFO (2019/2020 PRICES)

Adult Standing: £14.00
Adult Seating: £14.00
Senior Citizen Standing/Seating: £10.00
Ages 16 to 21 Standing/Seating: £10.00
Under-16s Standing: £2.00 (with a paying adult)
Under-16s Seating: £2.00 (with a paying adult)

DISABLED INFORMATION

Wheelchairs: Accommodated in dedicated areas of the ground
Helpers: Admitted
Prices: Normal prices for disabled fans. Free for helpers
Disabled Toilets: Available in Zones 3 and 8
Contact: (01773) 830277   (Bookings are not necessary)

Travelling Supporters' Information:
Routes: Exit the M1 at Junction 28 and take the A38 signposted for Derby. After 2 miles take the sliproad onto the B600 then go right at the main road towards the town centre. After ½ mile turn left down North Street and the ground is on the right after 200 yards.

ALTRINCHAM FC

Founded: 1891
Former Names: Broadheath FC
Nickname: 'The Robins'
Ground: The J. Davidson Stadium, Moss Lane, Altrincham   WA15 8AP
Record Attendance: 10,275 (February 1925)
Pitch Size: 110 × 72 yards
Web site: www.altrinchamfc.com

Colours: Red and White striped shirts, Black shorts
Telephone Nº: (0161) 928-1045
Fax Number: (0161) 926-9934
Ground Capacity: 6,085
Seating Capacity: 1,154
E-mail: office@altrinchamfootballclub.co.uk

GENERAL INFORMATION

Car Parking: The club has an agreement for supporters to use the Aecom car park (179 Moss Lane, WA14 8FH) on matchdays. This is just a short walk from the stadium.
Coach Parking: By Police Direction
Nearest Railway Station: Altrincham (15 minutes walk)
Nearest Bus Station: Altrincham
Club Shop: Inside the ground
Opening Times: Weekdays 9.00am to 5.00pm
Telephone Nº: (0161) 928-1045

GROUND INFORMATION

Away Supporters' Entrances & Sections:
Hale End turnstiles and accommodation

ADMISSION INFO (2019/2020 PRICES)

Adult Standing/Seating: £14.00
Senior Citizen/Student Standing/Seating: £11.00
Under-16s Standing/Seating: £5.00
Under-12s Standing/Seating: £1.00

DISABLED INFORMATION

Wheelchairs: 3 spaces are available each for home and away fans adjacent to the Away dugout
Helpers: Admitted
Prices: Normal prices apply for disabled supporters. Helpers are admitted free of charge
Disabled Toilets: Yes
Contact: (0161) 928-1045   (Bookings are necessary)

Travelling Supporters' Information:
Routes: Exit the M56 at either Junction 6 or 7 and follow the signs for Altrincham FC.

BLYTH SPARTANS AFC

Founded: 1899
Former Names: None
Nickname: 'Spartans'
Ground: Croft Park, Blyth, Northumberland, NE24 3JE
Record Attendance: 10,186 (1956)
Pitch Size: 110 × 70 yards

Colours: Green and White striped shirts, Black shorts
Telephone Nº: (01670) 352373 (Office)
Fax Number: (01670) 545592
Ground Capacity: 4,435
Seating Capacity: 556
Web site: www.blythspartans.com

GENERAL INFORMATION
Car Parking: At the ground
Coach Parking: At the ground
Nearest Railway Station: Newcastle
Nearest Bus Station: Blyth (5 minutes walk)
Club Shop: At the ground
Opening Times: Matchdays only
Telephone Nº: (01670) 352373

GROUND INFORMATION
Away Supporters' Entrances & Sections:
No usual segregation

ADMISSION INFO (2019/2020 PRICES)
Adult Standing: £12.00   **Adult Seating**: £14.00
Senior Citizen Standing: £7.00
Senior Citizen Seating: £9.00
Ages 11 to 16 & Student Standing: £5.00
Ages 11 to 16 & Student Seating: £7.00
Note: Under-11s are admitted free of charge when accompanied by a paying adult
Programme Price: £2.00

DISABLED INFORMATION
Wheelchairs: Accommodated
Helpers: Please phone the club for information
Prices: Adult disabled fans are charged the Senior Citizen rate shown above. Younger disabled fans charged lower rate.
Disabled Toilets: Available
Contact: (01670) 352373 (Bookings are necessary)

Travelling Supporters' Information:
Routes: Pass through the Tyne Tunnel and take the left lane for Morpeth (A19/A1). At the 2nd roundabout (after approximately 7 miles) take full right turn for the A189 (signposted Ashington). After 2 miles take the slip road (A1061 signposted Blyth). Follow signs for Blyth turning left at the caravan site. At the 2nd roundabout turn right and the ground is on the left.

BOSTON UNITED FC

Founded: 1933
Former Names: Boston Town FC & Boston Swifts FC
Nickname: 'The Pilgrims'
Ground: Jakemans Stadium, York Street, Boston,
PE21 6JN
Ground Capacity: 6,778 **Seating Capacity**: 4,708
Pitch Size: 112 × 72 yards
Record Attendance: 11,000 (vs Derby County, 1974)

Colours: Amber and Black striped shirts, Black shorts
Telephone Nº: (01205) 364406 (Office)
Matchday Info: (01205) 364406
Fax Number: (01205) 354063
Web Site: www.bostonunited.co.uk
E-mail: admin@bufc.co.uk

GENERAL INFORMATION

Car Parking: Permit holders only
Coach Parking: Available near to the ground
Nearest Railway Station: Boston (1 mile)
Nearest Bus Station: Boston Coach Station (¼ mile)
Club Shop: In the car park at the ground
Opening Times: Weekdays from 9.00am to 5.00pm and
Saturday Matchdays from 11.00am to 5.00pm
Telephone Nº: (01205) 364406

GROUND INFORMATION

Away Supporters' Entrances & Sections:
York Street Entrances 3 & 4 for accommodation in the
Lincolnshire Cooperative Stand (subject to a move to the
Jakemans Stand if so advised by the police)

ADMISSION INFO (2019/2020 PRICES)

Adult Standing: £13.00   **Adult Seating**: £15.00
Child Standing: £4.00
Child Seating: £5.00
Senior Citizen Standing: £10.00
Senior Citizen Seating: £11.00
Note: A range of discounted Family tickets are also available.
Programme Price: £3.00

DISABLED INFORMATION

Wheelchairs: 7 spaces available for home fans, 4 spaces for
away fans below the Main Stand at the Town End
Helpers: One helper admitted per disabled fan
Prices: £10.00 for disabled fans using wheelchairs. Free of
charge for helpers
Disabled Toilets: Available in the Town End Terrace
Contact: (01205) 364406 (Bookings are necessary)

Travelling Supporters' Information:
From the North: Take the A17 from Sleaford, bear right after the railway crossing to the traffic lights over the bridge. Go forward through the traffic lights into York Street for the ground; From the South: Take the A16 from Spalding and turn right at the traffic lights over the bridge. Go forward through the next traffic lights into York Street for the ground.

BRACKLEY TOWN FC

Founded: 1890
Former Names: None
Nickname: 'Saints'
Ground: St. James Park, Churchill Way, Brackley, NN13 7EJ
Record Attendance: 2,604 (12th May 2013)

Colours: Red and White shirts with White shorts
Telephone Nº: (01280) 704077
Ground Capacity: 3,500
Seating Capacity: 507
Web Site: www.brackleytownfc.com
E-mail: janenebutters@brackleytownfc.co.uk

GENERAL INFORMATION
Car Parking: At the ground (£2.00 charge per car)
Coach Parking: At the ground
Nearest Railway Station: King's Sutton (6¾ miles)
Club Shop: At the ground
Opening Times: Matchdays and by appointment only
Telephone Nº: (01280) 704077

GROUND INFORMATION
Away Supporters' Entrances & Sections:
No usual segregation

ADMISSION INFO (2019/2020 PRICES)
Adult Standing: £13.00
Adult Seating: £13.00
Senior Citizen/Student Standing: £8.00
Senior Citizen/Student Seating: £8.00
Under-18s Standing: £5.00
Under-18s Seating: £5.00
Under-10s Seating/Standing: Free of charge
Family Ticket: £30.00 (2 adults + 3 children)

DISABLED INFORMATION
Wheelchairs: Accommodated
Helpers: Admitted
Prices: Normal prices apply for the disabled. Free for helpers
Disabled Toilets: Available
Contact: (01280) 704077 (Stephen Toghill – bookings are necessary)

Travelling Supporters' Information:
Routes: From the West: Take the A422 to Brackley and take the first exit at the roundabout with the junction of the A43, heading north into Oxford Road.* Go straight on at the next roundabout and continue into Bridge Street before turning right into Churchill Way. The ground is located at the end of the road; From the South: Take the A43 northwards to Brackley. Take the second exit at the roundabout with the junction of the A422 and head into Oxford Road. Then as from * above; From the North-East: Take the A43 to Brackley. Upon reaching Brackley, take the 1st exit at the 1st roundabout, the 2nd exit at the next roundabout then the 3rd exit at the following roundabout into Oxford Road. Then as from * above.

BRADFORD PARK AVENUE FC

Founded: 1907   (Re-formed in 1988)
Former Names: None
Nickname: 'Avenue'
Ground: Horsfall Stadium, Cemetery Road, Bradford, BD6 2NG
Ground Capacity: 3,500   **Seating Capacity**: 1,800
Record Attendance: 2,100 (2003)
Pitch Size: 112 × 71 yards

Colours: Red, Yellow and Black hooped shirts with Black shorts and socks
Telephone Nº: (01274) 674584
Office Number: (01484) 400007
Web site: www.bpafc.com
E-mail: info@bpafc.com

GENERAL INFORMATION

Car Parking: Street parking and some spaces at the ground
Coach Parking: At the ground
Nearest Railway Station: Bradford Interchange (3 miles)
Nearest Bus Station: Bradford Interchange (3 miles)
Club Shop: At the ground
Opening Times: Matchdays only
Telephone Nº: (01274) 674584

GROUND INFORMATION

Away Supporters' Entrances & Sections:
Segregation only used when required

ADMISSION INFO (2019/2020 PRICES)

Adult Standing/Seating: £10.00
Senior Citizen Standing/Seating: £8.00
Student Standing/Seating: £8.00
Under-16s Standing/Seating: £1.00

DISABLED INFORMATION

Wheelchairs: Accommodated in front of the Stand
Helpers: Please phone the club for information
Prices: Please phone the club for information
Disabled Toilets: Available in the clubhouse
Contact: (01274) 674584   (Bookings are not necessary)

Travelling Supporters' Information:
Routes: Exit the M62 at Junction 26 and take the M606 to its end. At the roundabout go along the A6036 (signposted Halifax) and pass Odsal Stadium on the left. At the roundabout by Osdal take the 3rd exit (still A6036 Halifax). After just under 1 mile, turn left at the Kinderhaven Nursery into Cemetery Road. The ground is 150 yards on the left.

CHESTER FC

Founded: 1885
Former Names: Chester FC and Chester City FC
Nickname: 'Blues'
Ground: Swansway Chester Stadium, Bumpers Lane, Chester CH1 4LT
Pitch Size: 116 × 75 yards
Record Attendance: 5,987 (17th April 2004)

Colours: Blue and White striped shirts, White shorts
Ground Telephone Nº: (01244) 371376
Ticket Office: (01244) 371376
Ground Capacity: 5,376
Seating Capacity: 4,170
Web site: www.chesterfc.com
E-mail: info@chesterfc.com

GENERAL INFORMATION

Car Parking: Ample spaces available at the ground (£2.00)
Coach Parking: Available at the ground
Nearest Railway Station: Chester (2 miles)
Nearest Bus Station: Chester (1½ miles)
Club Shop: At the ground
Opening Times: Weekdays & matchdays 10.00am–4.00pm
Telephone Nº: (01244) 371376

GROUND INFORMATION

Away Supporters' Entrances & Sections:
South Stand for covered seating and also part of the West Stand

ADMISSION INFO (2019/2020 PRICES)

Adult Standing: £12.00   **Adult Seating**: £15.00
Senior Citizen/Concessions Standing: £10.00
Senior Citizen/Concessions Seating: £12.00
Ages 18 to 21 Seating/Standing: £10.00
Ages 5 to 17 Seating/Standing: £3.00
Ages 5 to 11 Seating: £1.00 in the Community Stand
Note: Under-5s are admitted free of charge

DISABLED INFORMATION

Wheelchairs: 32 spaces for wheelchairs (with 40 helpers) in the West Stand and East Stand
Helpers: Admitted
Prices: Normal prices for the disabled. Free for helpers
Disabled Toilets: Available in West and East Stands
Contact: (01244) 371376 (Bookings are necessary)

Travelling Supporters' Information:
Routes: From the North: Take the M56, A41 or A56 into the Town Centre and then follow Queensferry (A548) signs into Sealand Road. Turn left at the traffic lights by 'Tesco' into Bumpers Lane – the ground is ½ mile at the end of the road; From the East: Take the A54 or A51 into the Town Centre (then as North); From the South: Take the A41 or A483 into Town Centre (then as North); From the West: Take the A55, A494 or A548 and follow Queensferry signs towards Birkenhead (A494) and after 1¼ miles bear left onto the A548 (then as North); From the M6/M56 (Avoiding Town Centre): Take the M56 to Junction 16 (signposted Queensferry), turn left at the roundabout onto A5117, signposted Wales. At the next roundabout turn left onto the A5480 (signposted Chester) and after approximately 3 miles take the 3rd exit from the roundabout (signposted Sealand Road Industrial Parks). Go straight across 2 sets of traffic lights into Bumpers Lane. The ground is ½ mile on the right.

CURZON ASHTON FC

Founded: 1963
Former Names: None
Nickname: 'The Nash'
Ground: Tameside Stadium, Richmond Street, Ashton-under-Lyne OL7 9HG
Record Attendance: 3,210 (2007)
Pitch Size: 114 × 72 yards

Colours: Royal Blue shirts and shorts
Telephone N°: (0161) 330-6033
Fax Number: (0161) 339-8802
Ground Capacity: 3,673
Seating Capacity: 527
Web Site: www.curzon-ashton.co.uk
E-mail: rob@curzon-ashton.co.uk

GENERAL INFORMATION

Car Parking: At the ground
Coach Parking: At the ground
Nearest Railway Station: Ashton-under-Lyne (1 mile)
Club Shop: At the ground
Opening Times: Matchdays only
Telephone N°: (0161) 330-6033

GROUND INFORMATION

Away Supporters' Entrances & Sections:
No usual segregation

ADMISSION INFO (2019/2020 PRICES)

Adult Standing: £14.00
Adult Seating: £14.00
Senior Citizen/Student Standing: £7.00
Senior Citizen/Student Seating: £7.00
Under-16s Standing: £3.00
Under-16s Seating: £3.00
Programme Price: £2.00

DISABLED INFORMATION

Wheelchairs: Accommodated
Helpers: Admitted
Prices: Normal prices apply for the disabled and helpers
Disabled Toilets: Available
Contact: (0161) 330-6033   (Bookings are not necessary)

Travelling Supporters' Information:
Routes: Exit the M60 at Junction 23 and take the A6140 signposted for Ashton. Continue along the A6140 to the set of traffic lights with a Cinema on the right then turn left. Cross over a bridge and go straight across the mini-roundabout before turning left into the ground.

DARLINGTON FC

Founded: 1883 (Re-formed 2012)
Former Names: Successor to the club Darlington FC, formed as Darlington 1883 and renamed in 2017
Nickname: 'Darlo', 'The Quakers'
Ground: Blackwell Meadows, Grange Road, Darlington   DL1 5NR
Record Attendance: 3,000 (26th December 2016)
Pitch Size: 110 × 75 yards

Ground Capacity: 3,281
Seating Capacity: 588
Colours: Black and White hooped shirts, Black shorts
Contact Telephone Nº: None
Web Site: www.darlingtonfc.co.uk
E-mail: dave.watson@darlingtonfc.org

GENERAL INFORMATION

Car Parking: A limited number of spaces at Blackwell Meadows are available on a first-come, first-served basis with a £5.00 fee. Alternatively, use town centre car parks (1½ miles)
Coach Parking: Limited parking at the ground
Nearest Railway Station: Darlington (1½ miles)
Nearest Bus Station: Darlington Town Centre (1½ miles)
Club Shop: Quaker Retail at the Dolphin Centre, Darlington and at Mysportswear, Morton Park, Darlington
Opening Times: Weekdays 10.00am to 1.00pm.
Telephone Nº: 07488 564642 (Quaker Retail) and (01325) 488884 (Mysportswear)

GROUND INFORMATION

Away Supporters' Entrances & Sections:
No usual segregation

ADMISSION INFO (2019/2020 PRICES)

Adult Standing: £14.00
Adult Seating: £16.00
Concessionary Standing: £10.00
Concessionary Seating: £12.00
Under-18s Standing: £5.00
Under-18s Seating: £7.00
Under-11s Standing/Seating: Free of charge
Note: Tickets are cheaper if purchased in advance online.
Programme Price: £2.50

DISABLED INFORMATION

Wheelchairs: Accommodated
Helpers: Helpers are admitted
Prices: Concessionary prices for the disabled and helpers
Disabled Toilets: Available
Contact: dave.watson@darlingtonfc.org   (Bookings are necessary)

Travelling Supporters' Information:
Routes: From the South: Exit the A1(M) at Junction 57 and take the A66(M) towards Darlington. At the end of the motorway, continue onto the A66 and take the second exit at the next roundabout onto the A167 Darlington Road. Blackwell Meadows is on the right after 400 yards; From the North: Exit the A1(M) at Junction 59 and take the A167 to Darlington. Upon entering Darlington, continue along the A167, taking the second exit at the roundabout into North Road, the first exit at Northgate Roundabout onto St. Cuthbert's Way then following the road around around Darlington town centre into Victoria Road before turning left at the Baptist church into Grange Road. Blackwell Meadows in on the left after approximately 1 mile.

FARSLEY CELTIC AFC

Founded: 1908 (Original club)
Former Names: Farsley Celtic FC
Nickname: 'Villagers'
Ground: The Citadel, Newlands, Farsley, Leeds, LS28 5BE
Record Attendance: 2,462 (2006)
Pitch Size: 110 × 67 yards

Colours: White and Green hooped shirts with Green shorts
Telephone Nº: (0113) 255-7292
Ground Capacity: 4,000
Seating Capacity: 300
Web site: www.farsleyceltic.com
E-mail: office@farsleyceltic.com

GENERAL INFORMATION

Car Parking: Available at the ground
Coach Parking: Available at the ground
Nearest Railway Station: New Pudsey (1 mile)
Nearest Bus Station: Pudsey (1 mile)
Club Shop: At the ground
Opening Times: Weekday evenings 6.00pm – 11.00pm and weekends noon until 11.00pm
Telephone Nº: (0113) 255-7292

GROUND INFORMATION

Away Supporters' Entrances & Sections:
No usual segregation

ADMISSION INFO (2019/2020 PRICES)

Adult Standing: £10.00
Adult Seating: £10.00
Senior Citizen/Student/Under-18s Standing: £6.00
Senior Citizen/Student/Under-18s Seating: £6.00
Under-13s/Armed Forces/Emergency Services: Free
Programme Price: £2.00

DISABLED INFORMATION

Wheelchairs: Accommodated
Helpers: Please phone the club for information
Prices: Please phone the club for information
Disabled Toilets: Available
Contact: (0113) 255-7292   (Bookings are necessary)

Travelling Supporters' Information:
Routes: From the North: Take the A1 to Wetherby then the A58 to Leeds. After about 8 miles take the 3rd exit at the roundabout onto the A6120 Ring Road. Follow signs for Bradford for approximately 12 miles and at the 7th roundabout take the B6157 signposted Stanningley. Continue for ½ mile passing the Police Station on the left then turn left down New Street (at the Tradex Warehouse). Turn right into Newlands and the ground is situated at the end of the road next to a new housing development.

GATESHEAD FC

Founded: 1930   (Reformed in 1977)
Former Names: Gateshead United FC
Nickname: 'Tynesiders'
Ground: International Stadium, Neilson Road,
Gateshead   NE10 0EF
Record Attendance: 11,750   (vs Newcastle Utd, 1995)
Pitch Size: 110 × 70 yards

Colours: White shirts with Black shorts
Telephone Nº: (0191) 478-3883
Fax Number: (0191) 440-0404
Ground Capacity: 11,750 (All seats)
Web site: www.gateshead-fc.com
E-mail: info@gateshead-fc.com

GENERAL INFORMATION

Car Parking: At the stadium
Coach Parking: At the stadium
Nearest Railway Station: Gateshead Stadium Metro
(½ mile); Newcastle (British Rail) 1½ miles
Nearest Bus Station: Newcastle Coach Station, St. James'
Boulevard, Newcastle-upon-Tyne, NE1 4BW   (2½ miles)
Club Shop: At the stadium
Opening Times: Matchdays only
Telephone Nº: (0191) 478-3883

GROUND INFORMATION

Away Supporters' Entrances & Sections:
East Stand

ADMISSION INFO (2018/2019 PRICES)

Adult Seating: £15.00
Senior Citizen/Concessionary Seating: £8.00
Under-16s/Student Seating: £3.00
Family Ticket: £25.00 (2 Adults + 2 Children)
Note: Prices for the 2019/2020 season had not been
announced at the time of going to press. Please contact the
club for further information.

DISABLED INFORMATION

Wheelchairs: 5 spaces available each for home and away
fans by the trackside – Level access with automatic doors
Helpers: Admitted
Prices: Normal prices for the disabled. Helpers are admitted
free of charge.
Disabled Toilets: Available in the Reception Area and on
the 1st floor concourse – accessible by lift.
Contact: (0191) 478-3883   (Bookings are necessary)

Travelling Supporters' Information:
Routes: From the South: Take the A1(M) to Washington Services and fork right onto the A194(M) signposted Tyne Tunnel. At
the next roundabout, turn left onto the A184 signposted for Gateshead. The Stadium is on the right after 3 miles.

GLOUCESTER CITY AFC

Gloucester City are groundsharing with Evesham United FC for the 2019/2020 season.

Founded: 1889 (**Re-formed**: 1980)
Forner Names: Gloucester YMCA
Nickname: 'The Tigers'
Ground: The Spiers and Hartwell Jubilee Stadium, Cheltenham Road, Evesham   WR11 3LZ
Ground Capacity: 3,000
Seating Capacity: 300
Record Attendance: 8,326 (1956)

Pitch Size: 110 × 72 yards
Colours: Yellow and Black Striped shirts, Black shorts
Contact Address: Meadow Park, Arriva House, Sudmeadow Road, Hempsted, Gloucester GL2 5HS
Telephone Nº: None
Web Site: www.gloucestercityafc.com
E-mail: info@gcafc.co.uk

GENERAL INFORMATION
Car Parking: Available at the ground.
Coach Parking: At the ground
Nearest Railway Station: Evesham (1¾ miles)
Nearest Bus Station: Evesham (1½ miles)
Club Shop: At the ground
Opening Times: Matchdays only

GROUND INFORMATION
Away Supporters' Entrances & Sections:
No usual segregation

ADMISSION INFO (2019/2020 PRICES)
Adult Standing/Seating: £13.00
Under-18s Standing/Seating: £8.00
Under-16s Standing/Seating: £3.00
Note: Under-11s are admitted free with a paying adult

DISABLED INFORMATION
Wheelchairs: Accommodated
Helpers: Admitted free of charge
Prices: Normal prices apply for disabled fans
Disabled Toilets: Available
Contact: info@gcafc.co.uk

Travelling Supporters' Information:
Routes: From the North: Exit the M5 at Junction 7 and follow the B4084 through Pershore into Evesham. At the traffic lights with the River Avon and Bridge on the left, turn right into Cheltenham Road then continue through two sets of traffic lights passing the Tesco Garage and Ambulance Station on the left before reaching a roundabout. The ground is then on the right; From the South: Exit the M5 at Junction 9, take the 3rd exit and follow the A46 to Evesham. The ground is on the left by the roundabout on outskirts of Evesham; From the East: Take the A44 to Evesham then turn left onto the A46 at the roundabout on the outskirts of Evesham. Continue over the next roundabout passing the Strawberry Field public house and McDonalds on the right and the ground is straight on at the next roundabout.

GUISELEY AFC

Founded: 1909
Former Names: None
Nickname: 'The Lions'
Ground: Nethermoor Park, Otley Road, Guiseley, Leeds   LS20 8BT
Record Attendance: 3,366 (v Leeds United 26/7/18)
Pitch Size: 110 × 69 yards

Colours: White shirts with Royal Blue shorts and socks
Telephone Nº: 07507 750553
Social Club Phone Nº: (01943) 872872
Fax Number: (01943) 873223
Ground Capacity: 4,000
Seating Capacity: 518
Web site: www.guiseleyafc.co.uk
E-mail: admin@guiseleyafc.co.uk

GENERAL INFORMATION

Car Parking: At the ground and in Netherfield Road – Please do not park in Ings Crescent!
Coach Parking: At the ground
Nearest Railway Station: Guiseley (5 minute walk)
Nearest Bus Station: Bus Stop outside the ground
Club Shop: At the ground
Opening Times: Matchdays only
Telephone Nº: (01943) 879236 (weekdays)
Postal Sales: Yes

GROUND INFORMATION

Away Supporters' Entrances & Sections:
No usual segregation

ADMISSION INFO (2019/2020 PRICES)

Adult Standing: £13.00
Adult Seating: £13.00
Concessionary Standing/Seating: £9.00
Ages 11 to 18 Standing/Seating: £5.00
Under-11s Standing/Seating: £1.00 when accompanied by a paying adult

DISABLED INFORMATION

Wheelchairs: Accommodated
Helpers: Admitted
Prices: Normal prices for disabled fans. Free for helpers
Disabled Toilets: None
Contact: (01943) 879236 (Bookings are advisable)

Travelling Supporters' Information:
Routes: Exit the M62 at Junction 28 and take the Leeds Ring Road to the roundabout at the junction of the A65 at Horsforth. Turn left onto the A65 and pass through Rawdon to Guiseley keeping Morrison's supermarket on your left. Pass straight through the traffic lights with the Station pub or your right and the ground is on the right after ¼ mile, adjacent to the cricket field.

HEREFORD FC

Founded: 1924
Former Names: None
Nickname: 'United' 'The Bulls'
Ground: Edgar Street, Hereford   HR4 9JU
Record Attendance: 18,114 (4th January 1958)
Pitch Size: 110 × 70 yards

Colours: White shirts with Black shorts
Telephone N°: (01432) 268257
Ground Capacity: 4,913
Seating Capacity: 3,390
Web site: www.herefordfc.co.uk
E-mail: info@herefordfc.co.uk

GENERAL INFORMATION

Car Parking: Merton Meadow Car Park (Near the ground)
Coach Parking: Merton Meadow Car Park
Nearest Railway Station: Hereford (½ mile)
Nearest Bus Station: Commercial Road, Hereford
Club Shop: At the ground
Opening Times: Wednesday and Friday 10.00am – 4.00pm.
Midweek home games, 10.00am–4.00pm & 6.00pm–7.30pm,
Saturday Matchdays 12.00pm to 2.45pm.
Telephone N°: (01432) 268257

GROUND INFORMATION

Away Supporters' Entrances & Sections:
Edgar Street entrances for the Len Weston Stand and Terrace

ADMISSION INFO (2019/2020 PRICES)

Adult Standing: £14.00
Adult Seating: £16.00
Ages 16 to 18 Standing: £7.00
Ages 16 to 18 Seating: £8.00
Under-16s Standing/Seating: £2.00 (Under-5s free)
Concessionary Standing: £12.00
Concessionary Seating: £14.00

DISABLED INFORMATION

Wheelchairs: 7 spaces in total for Home and Away fans
Helpers: One helper admitted per disabled person
Prices: Concessionary prices for the disabled. Free for helpers
Disabled Toilets: Available in the Merton Stand
Contact: (01432) 268257 or 07596 263171 on Matchdays
E-mail: herefordfcdsa@gmail.com   (Bookings necessary)

Travelling Supporters' Information:
Routes: From the North: Follow A49 Hereford signs straight into Edgar Street; From the East: Take the A465 or A438 into Hereford Town Centre, then follow signs for Leominster (A49) into Edgar Street; From the South: Take the A49 or A45 into the Town Centre (then as East); From the West: Take the A438 into the Town Centre (then as East).

KETTERING TOWN FC

Founded: 1872
Former Names: Kettering FC
Nickname: 'The Poppies'
Ground: Latimer Park, Polwell Lane, Burton Latimer, Kettering NN15 5PS
Record Attendance: 11,526 (at Rockingham Road)
Pitch Size: 110 × 68 yards

Colours: Red shirts with Black shorts and socks
Telephone Nº: (01536) 217006
Ground Capacity: 2,500
Seating Capacity: 600
Web site: www.ketteringtownfc.com

GENERAL INFORMATION

Car Parking: At the ground
Coach Parking: At the ground
Nearest Railway Station: Kettering (3 miles)
Nearest Bus Station: Kettering
Club Shop: None

GROUND INFORMATION

Away Supporters' Entrances & Sections:
Please phone the club for further information

ADMISSION INFO (2019/2020 PRICES)

Adult Standing: £15.00
Adult Seating: £16.00
Concessionary Standing: £12.00
Concessionary Seating: £13.00
Under-16s Standing/Seating: £3.00
Note: The above prices may change during the season
Programme Price: £3.00

DISABLED INFORMATION

Wheelchairs: Accommodated around the ground
Helpers: Admitted
Prices: Normal prices apply for the disabled fans with registered carers admitted free of charge
Disabled Toilets: Available around the ground
Contact: 07881 827188 Neil Griffin (Secretary)

Travelling Supporters' Information:
Routes: The ground is located on the A6 about 350 yards north of the junction with the A45 (over the bridge). This is approximately 6 miles south of the A14.

KIDDERMINSTER HARRIERS FC

Founded: 1886
Nickname: 'Harriers'
Ground: Aggborough Stadium, Hoo Road,
Kidderminster DY10 1NB
Ground Capacity: 6,444
Seating Capacity: 3,140
Record Attendance: 9,155 (vs Hereford, 1948)

Pitch Size: 110 × 72 yards
Colours: Red shirts with White sleeves, Red shorts
Telephone Nº: (01562) 823931
Fax Number: (01562) 827329
Web Site: www.harriers.co.uk
E-mail: info@harriers.co.uk

GENERAL INFORMATION

Car Parking: At the ground (£3.00 to £5.00 per car)
Coach Parking: As directed
Nearest Railway Station: Kidderminster
Nearest Bus Station: Kidderminster Town Centre
Club Shop: At the ground
Opening Times: Weekdays 9.00am to 5.00pm. Saturday
matchdays 11.00am to 3.00pm then 4.45pm to 5.30pm and
midweek matchdays 9.00am to 8.00pm then for an hour
after the game.
Telephone Nº: (01562) 823931

GROUND INFORMATION

Away Supporters' Entrances & Sections:
East Stand for seating and South Stand Terrace for standing

ADMISSION INFO (2019/2020 PRICES)

Adult Standing: £15.00
Adult Seating: £17.00
Concessionary Standing: £9.00
Concessionary Seating: £12.00
Under-16s Standing: £1.00
Under-16s Seating: £5.00
Programme: £3.00
Note: Under-5s are admitted free with a paying adult.

DISABLED INFORMATION

Wheelchairs: Home fans accommodated at the front of the
Main Stand, Away fans in front of the East Stand
Helpers: Admitted
Prices: Normal prices for the disabled with one helper free
Disabled Toilets: Available by the disabled area
Contact: (01562) 823931   (Bookings are not necessary)

Travelling Supporters' Information:
Routes: Exit the M5 at Junction 3 and follow the A456 to Kidderminster. The ground is situated close by the Severn Valley
Railway Station so follow the brown Steam Train signs and turn into Hoo Road about 200 yards downhill of the station. Follow
the road along for ¼ mile and the ground is on the left.

KING'S LYNN TOWN FC

Founded: 1879
Former Names: Lynn Town FC, Lynn FC
Nickname: 'The Linnets'
Ground: The Walks Stadium, Tennyson Road,
King's Lynn   PE30 5PB
Record Attendance: 12,937 (vs Exeter City 1950/51)
Pitch Size: 115 × 78 yards

Colours: Blue shirts with Yellow trim, Yellow shorts
Telephone Nº: (01553) 760060
Fax Number: (01553) 762159
Ground Capacity: 8,200
Seating Capacity: 1,200
Web site: www.kltown.co.uk
E-mail: office@kltown.co.uk

GENERAL INFORMATION

Car Parking: At the ground
Coach Parking: At the ground
Nearest Railway Station: King's Lynn (¼ mile)
Nearest Bus Station: King's Lynn (¼ mile)
Club Shop: At the ground
Opening Times: Matchdays only
Telephone Nº: (01553) 760060

GROUND INFORMATION

Away Supporters' Entrances & Sections:
No usual segregation

ADMISSION INFO (2019/2020 PRICES)

Adult Standing: £15.00
Adult Seating: £17.00
Concessions Standing: £13.00
Concessions Seating: £15.00
Under-18s Standing: £9.00
Under-18s Seating: £11.00
Under-16s Standing/Seating: £2.00

DISABLED INFORMATION

Wheelchairs: Accommodated
Helpers: Please phone the club for information
Prices: Please phone the club for information
Disabled Toilets: Available
Contact: (01553) 760060   (Bookings are not necessary)

Travelling Supporters' Information:
Routes: From all directions: The A47/A17/A10 all meet at Hardwick Roundabout. At this roundabout follow signs for the town centre passing through two sets of traffic lights. After the second set of lights get in the right hand lane and take the 4th exit at the roundabout keeping the Car Sales outlet on the left. Continue for ½ mile into Tennyson Road and the ground is situated on the left hand side.

LEAMINGTON FC

Founded: 1891
Former Names: Leamington Town FC,
Lockheed Borg & Beck FC, AP Leamington FC and
Lockheed Leamington FC
Nickname: 'The Brakes'
Ground: The Phillips 66 Community Stadium,
Harbury Lane, Leamington Spa CV33 9QB
Record Attendance: 2,102 (1st May 2017)

Colours: Gold and Black shirts with Black shorts
Telephone Nº: (01926) 430406
Fax Number: (01926) 430406
Ground Capacity: 3,000
Seating Capacity: 294
Web Site: www.leamingtonfc.co.uk
E-mail: info@leamingtonfc.co.uk

GENERAL INFORMATION
Car Parking: At the ground
Coach Parking: At the ground
Nearest Railway Station: Leamington (4 miles)
Club Shop: At the ground plus online sales via the web site
Opening Times: Matchdays only
E-mail: shop@leamingtonfc.co.uk

GROUND INFORMATION
Away Supporters' Entrances & Sections:
No usual segregation

ADMISSION INFO (2019/2020 PRICES)
Adult Standing/Seating: £13.00
Concessionary Standing/Seating: £9.00
Under-18s Standing/Seating: £3.00 (Under-12s free)
Student Standing/Seating: £6.00

DISABLED INFORMATION
Wheelchairs: Accommodated
Helpers: Admitted
Prices: Normal prices apply for the disabled. Helpers are
admitted free of charge
Disabled Toilets: Available
Contact: (01926) 430406 (Bookings are not necessary)

Travelling Supporters' Information:
Routes: Exit the M40 at Junction 14 and take the A452 towards Leamington continuing at the roundabout into Europa Way
(still A452). After approximately ½ mile, take the 4th exit at the roundabout into Harbury Lane (signposted for Harbury and
Bishops Tachbrook). Continue on Harbury lane, taking the 3rd exit at the first roundabout and going straight ahead at the traffic
lights. The ground is on the left hand side of the road after approximately 1½ miles.   **SatNav**: CV33 9SA

SOUTHPORT FC

Founded: 1881
Former Names: Southport Vulcan FC, Southport Central FC
Nickname: 'The Sandgrounders' and 'The Port'
Ground: Merseyrail Community Stadium, Haig Avenue, Southport, Merseyside   PR8 6JZ
Record Attendance: 20,010 (vs Newcastle, 1932)
Pitch Size: 110 × 77 yards

Colours: Yellow shirts and shorts
Telephone Nº: (01704) 533422
Fax Number: (01704) 533455
Ground Capacity: 6,008
Seating Capacity: 1,660
Web site: www.southportfc.net

GENERAL INFORMATION

Car Parking: Street parking
Coach Parking: Adjacent to the ground
Nearest Railway Station: Meols Cop (½ mile)
Nearest Bus Station: Southport Town Centre
Club Shop: At the ground
Opening Times: Matchdays from 11.00am (from 6.30pm on evening matchdays)
Telephone Nº: (01704) 533422

GROUND INFORMATION

Away Supporters' Entrances & Sections:
Blowick End entrances

ADMISSION INFO (2019/2020 PRICES)

Adult Standing: £13.50
Adult Seating: £15.00
Concessionary Standing: £10.00
Concessionary Seating: £11.00
Under-19s Standing/Seating: £5.00
Note: Children aged 11 and under are admitted free of charge when accompanied by a paying adult.
Programme: £2.50

DISABLED INFORMATION

Wheelchairs: Accommodated in front of the Grandstand
Helpers: Admitted
Prices: Normal prices charged for the disabled. Helpers are admitted free of charge
Disabled Toilets: Available at the Blowick End of the Grandstand
Contact: (01704) 533422   (Bookings are not necessary)

Travelling Supporters' Information:
Routes: Exit the M58 at Junction 3 and take the A570 to Southport. At the major roundabout (McDonalds/Tesco) go straight on into Scarisbrick New Road, pass over the brook and turn right into Haig Avenue at the traffic lights. The ground is then on the right-hand side.

SPENNYMOOR TOWN FC

Founded: 2005 (Formed by the amalgamation of Evenwood Town and the defunct Spennymoor United)
Former Names: None
Nickname: 'The Moors'
Ground: The Brewery Field, Wood Vue, Spennymoor, Co. Durham   DL16 6JN
Record Attendance: 7,202 (30th March 1957)

Pitch Size: 104 × 65 yards
Colours: Black and White striped shirts, Black shorts
Telephone Nº: (01388) 827248 or Club Secretary on 07421 472240
Ground Capacity: 3,000
Seating Capacity: 742
Web Site: www.spennymoortownfc.co.uk

GENERAL INFORMATION

Car Parking: Street parking sometimes available but it can get very congested so fans are recommended to use the car parks behind the Town Hall or Leisure Centre.
Coach Parking: Please contact Steven Lawson on 07871 206474 for information
Nearest Railway Station: Durham (6 miles)
Nearest Bus Station: Durham – the No. 6 bus which stops in Durham Road, Spennymoor (15 minute journey)
Club Shop: At the ground
Opening Times: Matchdays only
Telephone Nº: (01388) 827248

GROUND INFORMATION

Away Supporters' Entrances & Sections:
Turnstile 7 for access to the Ramside Hall Estates Main Stand and the Motif8 Stand.

ADMISSION INFO (2019/2020 PRICES)

Adult Standing/Seating: £10.00 – £14.00
Over-60s Standing/Seating: £8.00 – £9.00
Under-18s Standing/Seating: £3.00 – £4.00
Note: Prices vary depending on the category of the game. Under-10s are admitted free with a paying adult
Programme Price: £2.50

DISABLED INFORMATION

Wheelchairs: Accommodated by arrangement. Entrance via the Wood Vue turnstiles and Tees Crescent
Helpers: One helper admitted per wheelchair
Prices: Normal prices are charged for fans with disabilities. Helpers are admitted free of charge
Disabled Toilets: 2 available in the ground
Contact: 07871 206474 (Steven Lawson)

Travelling Supporters' Information:
Routes: Exit the A1(M) at Junction 60 and follow the A689 to Rushyford. Take the 3rd exit at the Rushyford roundabout onto the A167 then the 3rd exit at the Chilton roundabout, continuing on the A167 towards Spennymoor. Take the first exit at the Thinford roundabout onto the A688, carry straight on at the small roundabout then take the 3rd exit at the next roundabout into St. Andrew's Lane. Continue along St. Andrew's Lane, turning left at the first roundabout then take the 2nd exit at the mini-roundabout, passing Asda into King Street, and the 2nd exit at the next mini-roundabout into Durham Road. Bear right along Durham Road and Wood Vue is on the left after a short distance.

YORK CITY FC

Please note that the club are scheduled to move to the York Community Stadium during the 2019/2020 season. However, the stadium is still under construction at the time of going to press so no opening date has yet been set. The new stadium is located in Kathryn Avenue in the Huntington area of the city, post code: YO32 9AF
Please contact the club for further information.

Founded: 1922
Nickname: 'The Minstermen'
Ground: Bootham Crescent, York   YO30 7AQ
Ground Capacity: 8,256   **Seating Capacity**: 3,409
Record Attendance: 28,123 (5th March 1938)
Pitch Size: 115 × 74 yards

Colours: Red shirts with Blue shorts
Telephone Nº: (01904) 624447 or (01904) 559500
Ticket Office: (01904) 559503 Extension 1
Fax Number: (01904) 631457
Web Site: www.yorkcityfootballclub.co.uk
E-mail: enquiries@yorkcityfootballclub.co.uk

GENERAL INFORMATION

Car Parking: Spaces are available in York Hospital car park (5 minutes walk) from 1.00pm (Saturday matches) and from 5.45pm (midweek matches). A voucher must be downloaded from the club's website to purchase a ticket and cost is £2.50.
Coach Parking: By Police direction
Nearest Railway Station: York (1 mile)
Club Shop: At the ground
Opening Times: Weekdays 11.00am – 3.00pm (but closed on Wednesdays); Saturday Matchdays 1.00pm–3.00pm and 4.40pm–5.30pm; Evening matches open from 6.00pm until kick-off then for 30 minutes after the final whistle.
Telephone Nº: (01904) 624447

GROUND INFORMATION

Away Supporters' Entrances & Sections:
Grosvenor Road turnstiles for Grosvenor Road End

ADMISSION INFO (2019/2020 PRICES)

Adult Standing: £14.00   **Adult Seating**: £15.00 – £19.00
Concessionary Standing: £10.00
Concessionary Seating: £11.00 – £14.00
Under-18s Standing: £5.00   **Seating**: £6.00 – £7.00
Under-5s Standing/Seating: Free of charge
Note: The above prices will also apply at the new stadium.

DISABLED INFORMATION

Wheelchairs: 18 spaces in total for Home and Away fans in the disabled section, in front of the Pitchside Bar
Helpers: One helper admitted per disabled person
Prices: £6.00 – £14.00 for fans with disabilities. Helpers are admitted free of charge
Disabled Toilets: Available at entrance to the disabled area
Contact: (01904) 624447 (Ext. 1) (Bookings not necessary) or e-mail: slo@yorkcityfootballclub.co.uk

Travelling Supporters' Information:
Routes: From the North: Take the A1 then the A59 following signs for York. Cross the railway bridge and turn left after 2 miles into Water End. Turn right at the end following City Centre signs for nearly ½ mile then turn left into Bootham Crescent; From the South: Take the A64 and turn left after Buckles Inn onto the Outer Ring Road. Turn right onto the A19, follow City Centre signs for 1½ miles then turn left into Bootham Crescent; From the East: Take the Outer Ring Road turning left onto the A19. Then as from the South; From the West: Take the Outer Ring Road turning right onto the A19. Then as from the South.

THE VANARAMA
NATIONAL LEAGUE SOUTH

Address

4th Floor, 20 Waterloo Street,
Birmingham   B2 5TB

Phone (0121) 643-3143

Web site   www.footballconference.co.uk

Clubs for the 2019/2020 Season

BATH CITY FC

Founded: 1889
Former Names: Bath AFC, Bath Railway FC and Bath Amateurs FC
Nickname: 'The Romans'
Ground: Twerton Park, Bath   BA2 1DB
Record Attendance: 18,020 (1960)
Pitch Size: 110 × 76 yards

Colours: Black and White striped shirts, Black shorts
Telephone N°: (01225) 423087
Ground Capacity: 3,500
Seating Capacity: 1,006
Web site: www.bathcityfc.com
E-mail: info@bathcityfootballclub.co.uk

GENERAL INFORMATION

Car Parking: 150 spaces available at the ground
Coach Parking: Available at the ground
Nearest Railway Station: Oldfield Park (1 mile)
Nearest Bus Station: Dorchester Street, Bath
Club Shop: Yes – c/o Club
Opening Times: Matchdays and office hours
Telephone N°: (01225) 423087

GROUND INFORMATION

Away Supporters' Entrances & Sections:
Turnstiles 17-19

ADMISSION INFO (2019/2020 PRICES)

Adult Standing/Seating: £13.00
Senior Citizen Standing/Seating: £10.00
Students/Under-18s Standing/Seating: £7.00
Under-16s Standing/Seating: £2.00
Family Tickets: £25.00 (2 adults + 2 children)

DISABLED INFORMATION

Wheelchairs: 10 spaces available each for home and away fans in front of the Family Stand
Helpers: Admitted
Prices: Normal prices for the disabled. Free for helpers
Disabled Toilets: Available behind the Family Stand
Contact: (01225) 423087   (Bookings are necessary)

Travelling Supporters' Information:
Route: As a recommendation, avoid exiting the M4 at Junction 18 as the road takes you through Bath City Centre. Instead, exit the M4 at Junction 19 onto the M32. Turn off the M32 at Junction 1 and follow the A4174 Bristol Ring Road south then join the A4 for Bath. On the A4, after passing through Saltford you will reach a roundabout shortly before entering Bath. Take the 2nd exit at this roundabout then follow the road before turning left into Newton Road at the bottom of the steep hill. The ground is then on the right hand side of the road.

BILLERICAY TOWN FC

Founded: 1880
Former Names: None
Nickname: 'Town' 'Blues'
Ground: The Steel Team Stadium, New Lodge, Blunts Wall Road, Billericay, Essex CM12 9SA
Ground Capacity: 5,000   **Seating Capacity**: 2,000
Record Attendance: 4,582 (vs West Ham, 2017)

Colours: Shirts are Royal Blue with White trim, shorts are White with Royal Blue trim
Telephone Nº: (01277) 286474
Web site: www.billericaytownfc.co.uk
E-mail: info@billericaytownfc.co.uk

GENERAL INFORMATION

Car Parking: Street parking only
Coach Parking: Please contact the club for information
Nearest Railway Station: Billericay (½ mile)
Club Shop: At the ground
Opening Times: Matchdays only
Telephone Nº: (01277) 652188

GROUND INFORMATION

Away Supporters' Entrances & Sections:
No usual segregation

ADMISSION INFO (2019/2020 PRICES)

Adult Standing/Seating: £13.00
Senior Citizen & Student Standing/Seating: £9.00
Under-18s Standing/Seating: £3.00
Under-11s Standing/Seating: £1.00
Family Ticket: £25.00 (2 adults + 2 Under-11s)

DISABLED INFORMATION

Wheelchairs: Accommodated
Helpers: Admitted
Prices: Normal prices apply
Disabled Toilets: Available in the Clubhouse
Contact: (01277) 286474 (Bookings are necessary)

Travelling Supporters' Information:
Route: Exit the M25 at Junction 28 and follow the A129 to Billericay. Turn right at the 1st set of traffic lights into Tye Common Road then 2nd right into Blunts Wall Road and the ground is on the right.
Alternative route: Exit the M25 at Junction 29 and take the A129 road from Basildon into Billericay and turn left at the 2nd set of traffic lights into Tye Common Road. Then as above.

BRAINTREE TOWN FC

Founded: 1898
Former Names: Manor Works FC, Crittall Athletic FC, Braintree & Crittall Athletic FC and Braintree FC
Nickname: 'The Iron'
Ground: Cressing Road Stadium, Clockhouse Way, Braintree, Essex   CM7 3DE
Record Attendance: 4,000 (May 1952)
Pitch Size: 110 × 70 yards

Ground Capacity: 4,222
Seating Capacity: 553
Colours: Orange shirts and socks with Blue shorts
Telephone Nº: (01376) 345617
Fax Number: (01376) 330976
Web site: www.braintreetownfc.org.uk
E-mail: braintreetfc@aol.com

GENERAL INFORMATION
Car Parking: At the ground
Coach Parking: At the ground
Nearest Railway Station: Braintree (1 mile)
Nearest Bus Station: Braintree
Club Shop: At the ground
Opening Times: Matchdays only
Telephone Nº: (01376) 345617

GROUND INFORMATION
Away Supporters' Entrances & Sections:
Gates 7-8 for accommodation in the Quag End

ADMISSION INFO (2019/2020 PRICES)
Adult Standing/Seating: £15.00
Concessionary Standing/Seating: £10.00
Under-18s Standing: £5.00

DISABLED INFORMATION
Wheelchairs: Accommodated – 6 spaces available in the Main Stand
Helpers: Admitted
Prices: Normal prices apply for fans with disabilities. Helpers are admitted free of charge
Disabled Toilets: Available
Contact: (01376) 345617

Travelling Supporters' Information:
Routes: Exit the A120 Braintree Bypass at the McDonald's roundabout and follow Cressing Road northwards. The floodlights at the ground are visible on the left ½ mile into town. Turn left into Clockhouse Way then left again for the ground.

CHELMSFORD CITY FC

Founded: 1938
Former Names: Chelmsford FC
Nickname: 'City' or 'Clarets'
Ground: Melbourne Community Stadium, Salerno Way, Chelmsford   CM1 2EH
Record Attendance: 16,807 (at New Writtle Street)
Pitch Size: 109 × 70 yards

Colours: Claret and White shirts and shorts
Telephone Nº: (01245) 290959
Ground Capacity: 3,000
Seating Capacity: 1,400
Web site: www.chelmsfordcityfc.com
E-mail: enquiries@chelmsfordcityfc.com

GENERAL INFORMATION

Car Parking: Limited space at ground and street parking
Coach Parking: Two spaces available at the ground subject to advance notice
Nearest Railway Station: Chelmsford (2 miles)
Nearest Bus Station: Chelmsford (2 miles)
Club Shop: At the ground
Opening Times: Matchdays only at present
Telephone Nº: (01245) 290959

GROUND INFORMATION

Away Supporters' Entrances & Sections:
No usual segregation

ADMISSION INFO (2019/2020 PRICES)

Adult Standing: £15.00
Adult Seating: £15.00
Under-18s Standing: £5.00
Under-18s Seating: £5.00
Under-12s Standing: Free of charge
Under-12s Seating: Free of charge
Concessionary Standing: £10.00
Concessionary Seating: £10.00

DISABLED INFORMATION

Wheelchairs: Spaces for 11 wheelchairs available
Helpers: Admitted free of charge
Prices: Normal prices apply for fans with disabilities
Disabled Toilets: Available
Contact: (01245) 290959   (Bookings are necessary)

Travelling Supporters' Information:
Route: The ground is situated next to the only set of high rise flats in Chelmsford which can therefore be used as a landmark. From the A12 from London: Exit the A12 at Junction 15 signposted for Chelmsford/Harlow/A414 and head towards Chelmsford along the dual-carriageway. At the third roundabout, immediately after passing the 'Superbowl' on the left, take the first exit into Westway, signposted for the Crematorium and Widford Industrial Estate. Continue along Westway which becomes Waterhouse Lane after the second set of traffic lights. At the next set of lights (at the gyratory system) take the first exit into Rainsford Road, signposted for Sawbridgeworth A1060. Continue along Rainsford Road then turn right into Chignal Road at the second set of traffic lights. Turn right again into Melbourne Avenue and Salerno Way is on the left at the end of the football pitches.

CHIPPENHAM TOWN FC

Founded: 1873
Former Names: None
Nickname: 'The Bluebirds'
Ground: Hardenhuish Park, Bristol Road, Chippenham, Wiltshire   SN14 6LR
Record Attendance: 4,800 (1951)
Pitch Size: 110 × 70 yards

Colours: Blue shirts, shorts and socks
Telephone N°: (01249) 650400
Contact N°: 07790 351004 (Club Secretary)
Fax Number: (01249) 650400
Ground Capacity: 3,000
Seating Capacity: 300
Web site: www.pitchero.com/clubs/chippenhamtown

GENERAL INFORMATION

Car Parking: Adjacent to the ground
Coach Parking: At the ground
Nearest Railway Station: Chippenham (1 mile)
Nearest Bus Station: Chippenham
Club Shop: At the ground
Opening Times: Matchdays only
Telephone N°: (01249) 650400

GROUND INFORMATION

Away Supporters' Entrances & Sections:
No usual segregation

ADMISSION INFO (2019/2020 PRICES)

Adult Standing: £10.00
Adult Seating: £11.00
Concessionary Standing: £6.00
Concessionary Seating: £7.00
Under-18s Standing: £3.00
Under-18s Seating: £4.00
Programme Price: £2.00

DISABLED INFORMATION

Wheelchairs: Accommodated at front of Stand
Helpers: Admitted
Prices: Normal prices apply for fans with disabilities. Helpers are admitted free of charge.
Disabled Toilets: None
Contact: (01249) 650400   (Bookings are not necessary)

Travelling Supporters' Information:
Routes: Exit the M4 at Junction 17 and take the A350. Turn right at the first roundabout and follow the road to the junction with the A420. Turn left following 'Town Centre' signs and the ground is just over ½ mile on the left near the Pelican crossing.

CONCORD RANGERS FC

Founded: 1967
Former Names: None
Nickname: 'The Beachboys'
Ground: Aspect Arena, Thames Road, Canvey Island, SS8 0HH
Record Attendance: 1,537 (vs Mansfield Town, 2014)

Colours: Yellow shirts with Yellow shorts
Telephone Nº: (01268) 515750
Ground Capacity: 3,250
Seating Capacity: 375
Web Site: www.concordrangers.co.uk
E-mail: media@concordrangers.co.uk

GENERAL INFORMATION
Car Parking: At the ground
Coach Parking: At the ground
Nearest Railway Station: Benfleet
Club Shop: None
Opening Times: –
Telephone Nº: –

GROUND INFORMATION
Away Supporters' Entrances & Sections:
No usual segregation

ADMISSION INFO (2018/2019 PRICES)
Adult Standing: £12.00
Adult Seating: £12.00
Senior Citizen Standing: £7.00
Senior Citizen Seating: £7.00
Ages 12 to 16 Standing/Seating: £3.00
Under-12s Standing/Seating: Free of charge
Note: Prices for the 2019/2020 season had not been set at the time of going to press. Please contact the club for details.

DISABLED INFORMATION
Wheelchairs: Accommodated
Helpers: Admitted
Prices: Normal prices apply for the disabled and helpers
Disabled Toilets: Available
Contact: (01268) 515750   (Bookings are necessary)

Travelling Supporters' Information:
Routes: Take the A13 to the A130 (Canvey Way) for Canvey Island. At the Benfleet roundabout, take the 3rd exit into Canvey Road and continue along through Charfleets Service Road into Long Road. Take the 5th turn on the right into Thorney Bay Road and Thames Road is the 3rd turn on the right. The ground is on the left-hand side around 300 yards down Thames Road.

DARTFORD FC

Founded: 1888
Former Names: None
Nickname: 'The Darts'
Ground: Princes Park Stadium, Grassbanks, Darenth Road, Dartford   DA1 1RT
Record Attendance: 4,097 (11th November 2006)
Pitch Size: 110 × 71 yards

Colours: White Shirts with Black Shorts
Telephone Nº: (01322) 299991
Fax Number: (01322) 299996
Ground Capacity: 4,118
Seating Capacity: 640
Web Site: www.dartfordfc.com
E-mail: info@dartfordfc.com

GENERAL INFORMATION

Car Parking: At the ground
Coach Parking: At the ground
Nearest Railway Station: Dartford (½ mile)
Nearest Bus Station: Dartford (½ mile) & Bluewater (2 miles)
Club Shop: At the ground
Opening Times: Matchdays only – 1.00pm to 6.00pm (but the stadium itself is open daily).
Telephone Nº: (01322) 299991

ADMISSION INFO (2019/2020 PRICES)

Adult Standing: £14.00
Adult Seating: £14.00
Senior Citizen/Concessionary Standing: £9.00
Senior Citizen/Concessionary Seating: £9.00
Youth (Ages 13 to 17) Standing/Seating: £5.00
Junior (Ages 5 to 12) Standing/Seating: £2.00
Under-5s Standing/Seating: Free of charge

DISABLED INFORMATION

Wheelchairs: 9 spaces available in total around the ground
Helpers: Admitted
Prices: Normal prices for the disabled. Free for helpers
Disabled Toilets: Available behind each goal, in the main reception and on the upper floor.
Contact: (01322) 299991   (Bookings are not necessary)

Travelling Supporters' Information:
Routes: From M25 Clockwise: Exit the M25 at Junction 1B. At the roundabout, take the 3rd exit onto Princes Road (A225) then the second exit at the next roundabout.* Continue downhill to the traffic lights (with the ground on the left), turn left into Darenth Road then take the 2nd left for the Car Park; From M25 Anti-clockwise: Exit the M25 at Junction 2 and follow the A225 to the roundabout. Take the first exit at this roundabout then the 2nd exit at the next roundabout. Then as from * above.

DORKING WANDERERS FC

Photo courtesy of John Mills @ Altius Photography

Founded: 1999
Former Names: None
Nickname: 'Wanderers'
Ground: Meadowbank Stadium, Mill Lane, Dorking, RH4 1DX
Record Attendance: 1,529 (29th December 2018)
Pitch Size: 110 × 70 yards

Colours: Red and White striped shirts with Blue shorts
Telephone Nº: (01306) 400151
Ground Capacity: 2,000
Seating Capacity: 300
Web site: www.dorkingwanderers.com
E-mail: info@dorkingwanderers.com

GENERAL INFORMATION

Car Parking: Limited number of spaces at the ground. St. Martins Walk car park is 2 minutes walk from the stadium.
Coach Parking: Please contact the club for information.
Nearest Railway Station: Dorking West (½ mile)
Nearest Bus Station: Nearest bus stop is at The White Hart (Stop K)
Club Shop: At the ground
Opening Times: Matchdays only plus online sales
Telephone Nº: (01306) 400151

GROUND INFORMATION

Away Supporters' Entrances & Sections:
No usual segregation

ADMISSION INFO (2019/2020 PRICES)

Adult Standing/Seating: £12.00
Concessionary Standing/Seating: £9.00
Under-18s Standing/Seating: £4.00
Under-8s Standing/Seating: Free of charge
Programme Price: £2.00

DISABLED INFORMATION

Wheelchairs: Accommodated
Helpers: Admitted
Prices: Please contact the club for details
Disabled Toilets: Available
Contact: (01306) 400151   (Bookings are necessary)

Travelling Supporters' Information:
Routes: From the North: Exit the M25 at Junction 9 and follow the A24 southwards to Dorking. Upon reaching Dorking, take the 3rd exit at the Deepdene Roundabout onto the A25 (Reigate Road) and continue into the High Street. Turn right into Mill Lane by The White Horse pub for the ground; From the South: Follow the A24 northwards to Dorking. Take the first exit at the Deepdene Roundabout onto Reigate Road, then as above; From the West: Follow the A25 eastwards to Dorking, continue into the High Street, then turn right by The White Horse pub into Mill Lane for the ground; From the East: Follow the A25 westward into Dorking, continue into the High Street, then turn left into Mill Lane for the ground.

DULWICH HAMLET FC

Photo courtesy of John Mills @ Altius Photography

Founded: 1893
Former Names: None
Nickname: 'The Hamlet'
Ground: Champion Hill Stadium, Edgar Kail Way, London SE22 8BD
Record Attendance: 3,104 (5th January 2019)
Pitch Size: 110 × 70 yards

Colours: Pink and Navy Blue quartered shirts with Navy Blue shorts
Telephone Nº: (0207) 274-8707
Fax Number: (0207) 501-9255
Ground Capacity: 3,000
Seating Capacity: 500
Web site: www.pitchero.com/clubs/dulwichhamlet

GENERAL INFORMATION

Car Parking: 50 spaces available at the ground
Coach Parking: At the ground
Nearest Railway Station: East Dulwich (adjacent)
Nearest Tube Station: Brixton (3½ miles)
Club Shop: At the ground
Opening Times: Matchdays only
Telephone Nº: (0207) 274-8707

GROUND INFORMATION

Away Supporters' Entrances & Sections:
No usual segregation

ADMISSION INFO (2019/2020 PRICES)

Adult Standing/Seating: £12.00
Concessionary Standing/Seating: £5.00
Note: Under-12s are admitted free of charge when accompanying a paying adult
Programme Price: £1.50

DISABLED INFORMATION

Wheelchairs: 10 spaces available in the front of the Main Stand
Helpers: Admitted
Prices: Normal prices apply for fans with disabilities. Helpers are admitted free of charge.
Disabled Toilets: Available behind the disabled area
Contact: (0207) 274-8707 (Bookings are necessary) – E-mail: commercial@dulwichhamletfc.co.uk

Travelling Supporters' Information:
Routes: From the Elephant & Castle: Go down Walworth Road, through Camberwell's one-way system and along Denmark Hill. Turn left by the railway into Champion Park and then right at the end down Grave Lane to the ground in Dog Kennel Hill; From the South: Come up through Streatham on the A23, turn right to Tulse Hill along the A205 (Christchurch Road) and carry on towards Sydenham. Turn left at The Grove into Lordship Lane and carry on to East Dulwich.

EASTBOURNE BOROUGH FC

Founded: 1963
Former Names: Langney Sports FC
Nickname: 'The Sports'
Ground: Langney Sports Club, Priory Lane, Langney, Eastbourne   BN23 7QH
Record Attendance: 3,770 (5th November 2005)
Pitch Size: 115 × 72 yards

Colours: Red shirts with Red and Black shorts
Telephone Nº: (01323) 766265
Fax Number: (01323) 741627
Ground Capacity: 4,400
Seating Capacity: 542
Web site: www.ebfc.co.uk
E-mail: info@ebfc.co.uk

GENERAL INFORMATION
Car Parking: Around 400 spaces available at the ground
Coach Parking: At the ground
Nearest Railway Station: Eastbourne (3 miles)
Nearest Bus Station: Eastbourne   (Service 6A to ground)
Club Shop: At the ground
Opening Times: Matchdays only
Telephone Nº: (01323) 766265

GROUND INFORMATION
Away Supporters' Entrances & Sections:
No usual segregation

ADMISSION INFO (2019/2020 PRICES)
Adult Standing: £13.00
Adult Seating: £13.00
Concessionary Standing/Seating: £9.00
Student Standing/Seating: £5.00
Under-18s Standing/Seating: £1.00

DISABLED INFORMATION
Wheelchairs: 6 spaces available
Helpers: Admitted
Prices: Normal prices apply for fans with disabilities. Free of charge for helpers
Disabled Toilets: Available
Contact: (01323) 766265   (Bookings are necessary)

Travelling Supporters' Information:
Routes: From the North: Exit the A22 onto the Polegate bypass, signposted A27 Eastbourne, Hastings & Bexhill. *Take the 2nd exit at the next roundabout for Stone Cross and Westham (A22) then the first exit at the following roundabout signposted Stone Cross and Westham. Turn right after ½ mile into Friday Street (B2104). At the end of Friday Street, turn left at the double mini-roundabout into Hide Hollow (B2191), passing Eastbourne Crematorium on your right. Turn right at the roundabout into Priory Road, and Priory Lane is about 200 yards down the road on the left; Approaching on the A27 from Brighton: Turn left at the Polegate traffic lights then take 2nd exit at the large roundabout to join the bypass. Then as from *.

HAMPTON & RICHMOND BOROUGH FC

Founded: 1921
Former Names: Hampton FC
Nickname: 'Beavers'
Ground: Jezzards Beveree Stadium, Beaver Close,
off Station Road, Hampton, Middlesex   TW12 2BX
Record Attendance: 3,225   (vs AFC Wimbledon, 2009)
Pitch Size: 113 × 71 yards

Colours: Blue and Red Striped shirts with Red shorts
Matchday Phone N°: (020) 8979-2456
Fax Number: (020) 8979-2456
Ground Capacity: 3,500
Seating Capacity: 644
Web site: www.hamptonfc.net

GENERAL INFORMATION

Car Parking: At the ground and street parking
Coach Parking: Contact the Club for information
Nearest Railway Station: Hampton
Nearest Bus Station: Hounslow/Kingston/Fulwell
Club Shop: At the ground
Opening Times: Matchdays only
Telephone N°: (020) 8979-2456

GROUND INFORMATION

Away Supporters' Entrances & Sections:
No usual segregation

ADMISSION INFO (2019/2020 PRICES)

Adult Standing: £13.00
Adult Seating: £13.00
Senior Citizen/Concessionary Standing: £8.00
Senior Citizen/Concessionary Seating: £8.00
Under-16s Standing/Seating: £3.00
Note: Under-5s are admitted free of charge
Programme Price: £2.50

DISABLED INFORMATION

Wheelchairs: Accommodated in front of the main stand
Helpers: Admitted
Prices: Normal prices apply
Disabled Toilets: Available
Contact: (020) 8979-2456   (Bookings are not necessary)

Travelling Supporters' Information:
Routes: From the South: Exit the M3 at Junction 1 and follow the A308 (signposted Kingston). Turn 1st left after Kempton Park into Percy Road. Turn right at the level crossing into Station Road then left into Beaver Close for the ground; From the North: Take the A305 from Twickenham then turn left onto the A311. Pass through Hampton Hill onto Hampton High Street. Turn right at the White Hart pub (just before the junction with the A308), then right into Station Road and right again into Beaver Close.

HAVANT & WATERLOOVILLE FC

Founded: 1998
Former Names: Formed by the amalgamation of Waterlooville FC and Havant Town FC
Nickname: 'The Hawks'
Ground: Westleigh Park, Martin Road, Havant, PO9 5TH
Record Attendance: 4,400 (2006/07)
Pitch Size: 111 × 70 yards

Colours: White shirts and shorts
Telephone Nº: (023) 9278-7822 (Ground)
Fax Number: (023) 9226-2367
Ground Capacity: 6,065
Seating Capacity: 655
Web site: www.havantandwaterloovillefc.co.uk

GENERAL INFORMATION

Car Parking: Space for 300 cars at the ground
Coach Parking: At the ground
Nearest Railway Station: Havant (1 mile)
Nearest Bus Station: Town Centre (1½ miles)
Club Shop: At the ground
Opening Times: Matchdays only
Telephone Nº: 07768 271143

GROUND INFORMATION

Away Supporters' Entrances & Sections:
Martin Road End

ADMISSION INFO (2019/2020 PRICES)

Adult Standing: £15.00
Adult Seating: £15.00
Senior Citizen Standing/Seating: £12.00
Concessionary Standing/Seating: £12.00
Note: When accompanied by a paying adult, children under the age of 11 are admitted free of charge

DISABLED INFORMATION

Wheelchairs: 12 spaces available in the Main Stand
Helpers: Admitted
Prices: Normal prices for disabled fans. Free for helpers
Disabled Toilets: Two available
Contact: (023) 9226-7822 (Bookings are necessary)

Travelling Supporters' Information:
Routes: From London or the North take the A27 from Chichester and exit at the B2149 turn-off for Havant. Take the 2nd exit off the dual carriageway into Bartons Road and then the 1st right into Martin Road for the ground; From the West: Take the M27 then the A27 to the Petersfield exit. Then as above.

HEMEL HEMPSTEAD TOWN FC

Founded: 1885
Former Names: Apsley FC and Hemel Hempstead FC
Nickname: 'The Tudors'
Ground: Vauxhall Road, Adeyfield, Hemel Hempstead HP2 4HW
Record Attendance: 2,840 (vs Gosport Borough 6th May 2013)
Pitch Size: 112 × 72 yards

Colours: Shirts and Shorts are Red with White trim
Telephone Nº: (01442) 251521 or (01442) 259777
Fax Number: (01442) 264322
Ground Capacity: 3,152
Seating Capacity: 534
Web site: www.hemelfc.com
E-mail: info@hemelfc.com

GENERAL INFORMATION
Car Parking: At the ground
Coach Parking: At the ground
Nearest Railway Station: Hemel Hempstead (1½ miles)
Nearest Bus Station: Hemel Hempstead (¾ mile)
Club Shop: At the ground
Opening Times: Matchdays only

GROUND INFORMATION
Away Supporters' Entrances & Sections:
No usual segregation

ADMISSION INFO (2019/2020 PRICES)
Adult Standing/Seating: £14.00
Concessionary Standing/Seating: £9.00
Under-18s Standing/Seating: £5.00
Under-5s Standing/Seating: Free of charge
Note: Under-16s are admitted for £1.00 with a paying adult
Programme Price: £2.50

DISABLED INFORMATION
Wheelchairs: Accommodated
Helpers: Admitted
Prices: Normal prices apply
Disabled Toilets: Available in the Clubhouse
Contact: (01442) 259777

Travelling Supporters' Information:
Routes: Exit the M1 at Junction 8 and go straight ahead at the first roundabout. When approaching the 2nd roundabout move into the right hand lane and, as you continue straight across be ready to turn right almost immediately through a gap in the central reservation. This turn-off is Leverstock Green Road and continue along this to the double mini-roundabout. At this roundabout turn left into Vauxhall Road and the ground is on the right at the next roundabout.

HUNGERFORD TOWN FC

Founded: 1886
Former Names: Hungerford Swifts FC
Nickname: 'The Crusaders'
Ground: Town Ground, Bulpit Lane, Hungerford, RG17 0AY
Record Attendance: 1,684 (vs Sudbury Town)

Colours: White shirts with Black shorts
Contact Telephone Nº: (01488) 682939
Ground Capacity: 2,500
Seating Capacity: 170
Web: www.hungerfordtown.com

GENERAL INFORMATION

Car Parking: At the ground and at the local school
Coach Parking: At the ground
Nearest Railway Station: Hungerford (½ mile)
Club Shop: At the ground
Opening Times: Matchdays only
Telephone Nº: (01488) 682939

GROUND INFORMATION

Away Supporters' Entrances & Sections:
No usual segregation

ADMISSION INFO (2019/2020 PRICES)

Adult Standing/Seating: £12.00
Concessionary Standing/Seating: £6.00
Under-16s Standing/Seating: £6.00
Note: Under-14s are admitted free of charge when accompanied by a paying adult
Programme Price: £2.00

DISABLED INFORMATION

Wheelchairs: Accommodated
Helpers: Admitted free of charge
Prices: Concessionary prices for the disabled.
Disabled Toilets: Available
Contact: (01488) 682939   (Bookings are not necessary)

Travelling Supporters' Information:
Routes: Exit the M4 at Junction 14 and take the A338 towards Hungerford. Upon reaching Hungerford, turn right at the roundabout onto the A4 Bath Road, turn left at the next rounabout into Charnham Street then turn left again into Bridge Street (A338). The road becomes the High Street and pass under the railway line, carry straight on over three mini-roundabouts then take the next left into Priory Road. Continue to the end of the street and continue left into Priory Road then take the 3rd turning on the left into Bulpit Lane. The entrance to the ground is on the left shortly after crossing the junction with Priory Avenue.

MAIDSTONE UNITED FC

Founded: 1992 (Reformed)
Former Names: Maidstone Invicta FC
Nickname: 'The Stones'
Ground: Gallagher Stadium, James Whatman Way, Maidstone ME14 1LQ
Record Attendance: 3,409 (29th April 2017)

Colours: Amber shirts with Black shorts
Telephone Nº: (01622) 753817
Ground Capacity: 4,191
Seating Capacity: 750
Web Site: www.maidstoneunited.co.uk

GENERAL INFORMATION

Car Parking: Various Pay & Display Car Parks available near the ground
Coach Parking: Maidstone coach park (1¼ miles) – please contact the club for further information
Nearest Railway Station: Maidstone East (¼ mile)
Club Shop: Available at the ground
Opening Times: Saturday Matchdays 12.30pm to 5.00pm; Tuesday Matchdays 6.15pm to 9.30pm.
Telephone Nº: (01622) 753817

GROUND INFORMATION

Away Supporters' Entrances & Sections:
No usual segregation – use the main turnstiles unless otherwise advertised.

ADMISSION INFO (2019/2020 PRICES)

Adult Standing: £15.00
Adult Seating: £18.00
Senior Citizen/Student Standing: £12.00
Senior Citizen/Student Seating: £15.00
Ages 11 to 16 Standing: £7.00
Ages 11 to 16 Seating: £10.00
Under-11s Standing: £2.00
Under-11s Seating: £5.00
Programme Price: £3.00

DISABLED INFORMATION

Wheelchairs: Accommodated
Helpers: Admitted
Prices: Normal prices apply for the disabled. Free for helpers
Disabled Toilets: Available
Contact: (01622) 753817 (Bookings are essential)

Travelling Supporters' Information:
Routes: Exit the M20 at Junction 6 or the M2 at Junction 3 and follow the A229 into Maidstone. After entering Maidstone, at the second roundabout (by the White Rabbit pub), take the third exit into James Whatman Way for the stadium. Please check the club web site for details of the nearest car parks.

OXFORD CITY FC

Founded: 1882
Former Names: None
Nickname: 'City'
Ground: Court Place Farm, Marsh Lane, Marston, Oxford   OX3 0NQ
Record Attendance: 9,500 (vs Leytonstone, 1950)

Colours: Blue & White hooped shirts with Blue shorts
Telephone Nº: (01865) 750906
Ground Capacity: 3,218
Seating Capacity: 520
Web Site: www.oxfordcityfc.co.uk
E-mail: ctoxford@btinternet.com

GENERAL INFORMATION

Car Parking: At the ground
Coach Parking: At the ground
Nearest Railway Station: Oxford (3¾ miles)
Club Shop: At the ground
Opening Times: Matchdays only
Telephone Nº: (01865) 744493

GROUND INFORMATION

Away Supporters' Entrances & Sections:
No usual segregation

ADMISSION INFO (2019/2020 PRICES)

Adult Standing: £12.00
Adult Seating: £12.00
Concessionary/Student Standing: £6.00
Concessionary/Student Seating: £6.00
Under-16s Standing: £2.00
Under-16s Seating: £2.00
Note: Under-5s are admitted free of charge

DISABLED INFORMATION

Wheelchairs: Accommodated
Helpers: Admitted
Prices: Normal prices apply for the disabled and helpers
Disabled Toilets: Available
Contact: (01865) 744493   (Bookings are not necessary)

Travelling Supporters' Information:
Routes: The stadium is located by the side of the A40 Northern Bypass Road next to the Marston flyover junction to the north east of Oxford. Exit the A40 at the Marston junction and head into Marsh Lane (B4150). Take the first turn on the left into the OXSRAD Complex then turn immediately left again to follow the approach road to the stadium in the far corner of the site.

SLOUGH TOWN FC

Image courtesy of Gary House Photography

Founded: 1890
Former Names: Slough FC and Slough United FC
Nickname: 'The Rebels'
Ground: Arbour Park, Stoke Road, Slough SL2 5AY
Record Attendance: 1,950
(vs Rochdale, 4/12/2017)
Contact Telephone N°: 07792 126124

Colours: Shirts are Amber with Navy Blue sleeves, shorts are Navy Blue
Ground Capacity: 2,000
Seating Capacity: 548
Web site: www.sloughtownfc.net
E-mail: gensec@sloughtownfc.net

GENERAL INFORMATION

Car Parking: At the ground, at St. Joseph's Catholic High School and in other local car parks
Coach Parking: At the ground
Nearest Railway Station: Slough (¾ mile)
Nearest Bus Station: Slough (¾ mile)
Club Shop: At the ground
Opening Times: Matchdays only
Telephone N°: 07933 221337 (Sue Shiel)

GROUND INFORMATION

Away Supporters' Entrances & Sections:
No usual segregation

ADMISSION INFO (2019/2020 PRICES)

Adult Standing/Seating: £13.00
Concessions Standing/Seating: £9.00
Under-18s Standing/Seating: £5.00
Under-16s Standing/Seating: £3.00 (Under-5s free)
Note: Under-12s must be accompanied by an adult.
Programme Price: £1.50

DISABLED INFORMATION

Wheelchairs: Accommodated
Helpers: Admitted. A free carers pass is available.
Download the relevant form from the club's web site.
Prices: Normal prices apply for the disabled and helpers
Disabled Toilets: Available
Contact: 07792 126124 (Bookings are not necessary) –
E-mail: gensec@sloughtownfc.net

Travelling Supporters' Information:
Routes: From the South: Exit the M4 at Junction 5 and head west on the A4 (London Road) for approximately 2¾ miles. Pass the Tesco Extra store and the turning to Slough Railway station on your right then turn right onto Stoke Road (B416). Continue along Stoke Road for ¾ mile then Arbour Park is on the right; From the North: Exit the M40 at Junction 2 and head south on the A355 towards Slough. After approximately 1½ miles, turn left onto Parish Lane by the Indian Courtyard and at the end of the road, turn right onto Windsor Road (B416). After 2 miles take the second exit at the roundabout, continuing on the B416 and Arbour Park is on the left after approximately 1 mile.

ST. ALBANS CITY FC

Founded: 1908
Former Names: None
Nickname: 'The Saints'
Ground: Clarence Park, York Road, St. Albans, Hertfordshire AL1 4PL
Record Attendance: 9,757 (27th February 1926)
Pitch Size: 110 × 80 yards

Colours: Blue shirts with Yellow trim, Blue shorts
Telephone Nº: (01727) 848914
Fax Number: (01727) 848914
Ground Capacity: 5,007
Seating Capacity: 642
Web site: www.stalbanscityfc.com

GENERAL INFORMATION

Car Parking: Street parking or in the railway station car park
Coach Parking: In Clarence Park
Nearest Railway Station: St. Albans City (200 yds)
Club Shop: At the ground
Opening Times: Matchdays only
Telephone Nº: (01727) 848914

GROUND INFORMATION

Away Supporters' Entrances & Sections:
No usual segregation but the South Stand can be used for away fans if necessary.

ADMISSION INFO (2019/2020 PRICES)

Adult Standing/Seating: £18.00
Concessionary Standing/Seating: £12.00
Under-16s Standing/Seating: £8.00
Note: Under-12s are admitted free of charge when accompanied by a paying adult
Programme Price: £2.50

DISABLED INFORMATION

Wheelchairs: Accommodated
Helpers: One admitted per disabled supporter
Prices: Normal prices for the disabled. Helpers free of charge
Disabled Toilets: Available in the York Road End
Contact: (01727) 848914 (Bookings are not necessary)

Travelling Supporters' Information:
Routes: Take the M1 or M10 to the A405 North Orbital Road and at the roundabout at the start of the M10, go north on the A5183 (Watling Street). Turn right along St. Stephen's Hill and carry along into St. Albans. Continue up Holywell Hill, go through two sets of traffic lights and at the end of St. Peter's Street, take a right turn at the roundabout into Hatfield Road. Follow over the mini-roundabouts and at the second set of traffic lights turn left into Clarence Road and the ground is on the left. Park in Clarence Road and enter the ground via the Park or in York Road and use the entrance by the footbridge.

TONBRIDGE ANGELS FC

Founded: 1948
Former Names: Tonbridge FC
Nickname: 'The Angels'
Ground: Longmead Stadium, Darenth Avenue, Tonbridge TN10 3JF
Record Attendance: 2,411 (2011)

Colours: Blue and White shirts with White shorts
Telephone Nº: (01732) 352417
Ground Capacity: 3,014
Seating Capacity: 774
Web site: www.tonbridgeangels.co.uk
E-mail: chcole1063@aol.com

GENERAL INFORMATION
Car Parking: At the ground
Coach Parking: At the ground
Nearest Railway Station: Tonbridge (2 miles)
Club Shop: At the ground
Opening Times: Matchdays only
Telephone Nº: (01732) 352417

GROUND INFORMATION
Away Supporters' Entrances & Sections:
No usual segregation

ADMISSION INFO (2019/2020 PRICES)
Adult Standing: £13.00
Adult Seating: £14.00
Student/Senior Citizen Standing: £9.00
Student/Senior Citizen Seating: £10.00
Under-12s Standing: £4.00
Under-12s Seating: £5.00

DISABLED INFORMATION
Wheelchairs: Accommodated
Helpers: Admitted
Prices: Normal prices apply
Disabled Toilets: One available
Contact: (01732) 352417

Travelling Supporters' Information:
Routes: Take the A26 or A21 to Tonbridge Town Centre, pass through the High Street and head north up Shipbourne Road which is the A227 Gravesend road. Turn left at the 2nd mini-roundabout by the 'Pinnacles' Pub into Darenth Avenue. The ground is situated at the bottom end of Darenth Avenue.

WEALDSTONE FC

Founded: 1899
Former Names: None
Nickname: 'The Stones' or 'The Royals'
Ground: Grosvenor Vale, Ruislip HA4 6JQ
Record Attendance: 2,469 (vs Colchester Utd, 2015)
Colours: Royal Blue shirts with White shorts

Telephone Nº: 07790 038095
Ground Capacity: 3,432
Seating Capacity: 698
Web site: www.wealdstone-fc.com
E-mail: wealdstonefc@btinternet.com

GENERAL INFORMATION

Car Parking: 100 spaces available at the ground
Coach Parking: Available outside the ground
Nearest Mainline Station: West Ruislip (1 mile)
Nearest Tube Station: Ruislip (½ mile)
Club Shop: Yes
Opening Times: Orders through the post only
Telephone Nº: –

GROUND INFORMATION

Away Supporters' Entrances & Sections:
No usual segregation

ADMISSION INFO (2019/2020 PRICES)

Adult Standing/Seating: £13.00
Concessionary Standing/Seating: £9.00
Under-18s Standing/Seating: £6.00
Note: Under-14s are admitted free of charge when accompanied by a paying adult
Programme Price: £3.00

DISABLED INFORMATION

Wheelchairs: Accommodated
Helpers: Admitted
Prices: Normal prices apply
Disabled Toilets: Available
Contact: (01895) 637487

Travelling Supporters' Information:
Routes: Exit the M25 at Junction 16 and take the A40 towards Uxbridge. At the Polish War Memorial Junction with the A4180, follow the Ruislip signs (West End Road). After about 1½ miles, turn right into Grosvenor Vale for the ground.

WELLING UNITED FC

Founded: 1963
Former Names: None
Nickname: 'The Wings'
Ground: Park View Road, Welling, Kent DA16 1SY
Record Attendance: 4,100 (vs Gillingham, 1989)
Pitch Size: 112 × 72 yards

Colours: Shirts are Red with White trim, Red shorts
Telephone Nº: (0208) 301-1196
Ground Capacity: 4,500
Seating Capacity: 1,000
Web site: www.wellingunited.com

GENERAL INFORMATION

Car Parking: Street parking only
Coach Parking: Outside of the ground
Nearest Railway Station: Welling (¾ mile)
Nearest Bus Station: Bexleyheath
Club Shop: At the ground
Opening Times: Matchdays only
Telephone Nº: (0208) 301-1196

GROUND INFORMATION

Away Supporters' Entrances & Sections:
Accommodation in the Danson Park End and the East Stand

ADMISSION INFO (2019/2020 PRICES)

Adult Standing: £13.00   **Adult Seating**: £15.00
Concessionary Standing: £9.00
Concessionary Seating: £11.00
Under-18s Standing: £5.00
Under-18s Seating: £7.00
Under-12s Standing: Free with a paying adult
Under-12s Seating: £2.00 with a paying adult
Programme Price: £3.00

DISABLED INFORMATION

Wheelchairs: Accommodated at the side of the Main Stand
Helpers: Admitted
Prices: Concessionary prices for fans with disabilities.
Helpers are admitted free of charge
Disabled Toilets: Yes
Contact: (0208) 301-1196   (Bookings are not necessary)

Travelling Supporters' Information:
Routes: Take the A2 (Rochester Way) from London, then the A221 Northwards (Danson Road) to Bexleyheath. At the end turn left towards Welling along Park View Road and the ground is on the left.

WEYMOUTH FC

Founded: 1890
Former Names: None
Nickname: 'Terras'
Ground: Bob Lucas Stadium, Radipole Lane, Weymouth, Dorset   DT4 9XJ
Ground Capacity: 6,600   **Seating Capacity**: 900
Record Attendance: 6,500 (14th November 2005)

Colours: Shirts are Claret with Sky Blue trim, shorts are Claret
Telephone Nº: (01305) 785558
Fax Number: 0844 310-4730
Web site: www.theterras.com
E-mail: info@theterras.com

GENERAL INFORMATION

Car Parking: 200 spaces available at the ground
Coach Parking: At the ground
Nearest Railway Station: Weymouth (2 miles)
Nearest Bus Station: Weymouth Town Centre
Club Shop: At the ground
Opening Times: Matchdays only
Telephone Nº: (01305) 785558

GROUND INFORMATION

Away Supporters' Entrances & Sections:
No usual segregation

ADMISSION INFO (2019/2020 PRICES)

Adult Standing: £14.00
Adult Seating: £14.00
Concessionary Standing: £10.00
Concessionary Seating: £10.00
Under-16s Standing: £3.00
Under-16s Seating: £3.00

DISABLED INFORMATION

Wheelchairs: Accommodated
Helpers: Admitted
Prices: Concessionary prices apply for the disabled. Helpers are admitted free of charge
Disabled Toilets: Available
Contact: (01305) 785558   (Bookings are not necessary)

Travelling Supporters' Information:
Routes: Take the A354 from Dorchester to Weymouth and turn right at the first roundabout to the town centre. Take the 3rd exit at the next roundabout and follow signs for the ground which is about ½ mile on the right.

National League 2018/2019 Season

	AFC Fylde	Aldershot Town	Barnet	Barrow	Boreham Wood	Braintree Town	Bromley	Chester City	Dagenham & Redbridge	Dover Athletic	Eastleigh United	Ebbsfleet United	FC Halifax Town	Gateshead	Harrogate Town	Hartlepool United	Havant & Waterlooville	Leyton Orient	Maidenhead United	Maidstone United	Salford City	Solihull Moors	Sutton United	Wrexham
Fylde		3-0	1-0	0-0	2-1	3-0	2-1	0-1	1-1	4-0	4-2	2-0	0-2	1-0	0-0	4-2	6-2	1-3	2-1	2-0	0-2	3-1	2-2	2-0
Aldershot Town	0-0		0-0	0-2	1-1	1-0	3-2	0-2	2-1	2-0	1-3	0-2	3-0	0-2	0-2	1-1	2-0	1-2	0-0	0-1	0-1	0-3	2-1	0-0
Barnet	1-1	2-0		3-1	1-1	1-1	1-1	0-2	2-1	2-0	1-2	0-3	1-1	1-2	1-0	0-0	2-2	0-0	1-0	0-2	1-3	2-0	0-1	1-2
Barrow	1-1	2-1	0-2		1-2	1-0	1-1	3-2	0-1	2-3	0-3	0-0	0-0	1-2	2-2	1-0	3-0	2-3	2-0	1-0	3-2	1-2	2-1	0-0
Boreham Wood	1-1	0-2	1-0	1-1		1-1	2-1	1-0	1-0	0-1	3-3	0-0	2-1	1-1	2-4	0-4	1-3	1-0	3-1	0-1	2-3	2-2	1-2	0-2
Braintree Town	2-1	0-1	4-0	0-2	1-1		2-4	1-3	2-0	2-1	1-2	0-4	0-2	2-0	0-4	1-1	3-4	1-5	0-2	0-1	1-0	0-3	2-2	0-1
Bromley	3-2	2-2	0-1	2-1	0-2	2-4		3-3	0-2	2-2	0-1	5-1	2-2	1-0	1-1	4-0	4-0	2-1	1-0	2-0	0-2	0-2	2-1	2-0
Chesterfield	0-0	3-0	0-1	0-0	3-2	1-0	1-1		2-0	0-0	2-3	3-3	1-0	0-3	0-1	1-1	0-0	0-1	1-3	4-1	2-0	0-4	3-0	1-1
Dagenham & Redbridge	2-1	1-1	0-1	0-0	4-4	1-0	3-0	1-1		1-3	2-0	1-3	1-1	0-2	2-1	1-2	3-1	2-1	2-2	1-2	0-0	1-1	1-0	1-2
Dover Athletic	2-1	1-0	1-2	0-2	1-1	3-0	1-1	0-0	0-2		1-2	1-1	2-1	1-2	2-3	2-1	4-3	0-0	2-0	3-1	1-4	0-2	3-0	0-1
Eastleigh	0-0	1-2	0-3	0-1	1-0	2-1	1-0	1-1	1-0	2-2		0-1	0-1	1-1	3-2	2-1	1-1	2-0	2-0	1-1	1-2	3-2		1-3
Ebbsfleet United	1-3	3-1	1-0	1-0	3-2	4-2	1-2	0-1	0-1	0-1	3-0		4-0	0-1	0-2	0-0	1-1	2-0	3-0	1-1	0-1	0-1	0-1	4-2
FC Halifax Town	0-0	0-0	3-0	2-0	1-1	0-0	2-2	1-1	2-1	1-0	0-1	0-0		1-0	1-1	1-2	0-0	1-1	0-1	3-0	2-0	0-1	2-1	
Gateshead	0-1	3-0	2-1	0-2	1-1	0-1	2-0	1-0	2-0	2-1	0-1	1-1	1-1		2-3	2-1	0-0	1-1	0-1	1-1	1-2	0-0	1-1	0-1
Harrogate Town	1-2	4-1	2-0	4-2	0-1	3-1	1-0	1-1	1-1	2-2	4-0	1-2	1-2	2-0		3-1	3-2	0-3	1-0	2-2	0-1	3-1	2-2	0-0
Hartlepool United	1-2	1-1	1-3	0-0	2-0	2-1	1-2	1-0	1-2	3-2	1-1	0-1	2-1	2-1	2-2		1-1	1-1	2-1	1-2	3-2	0-1	2-3	1-0
Havant & Waterlooville	1-1	2-1	0-2	2-0	0-0	2-1	0-3	1-2	3-0	0-0	2-2	3-3	2-1	0-1	1-2	1-2		1-2	7-0	5-2	1-1	0-1	1-2	2-3
Leyton Orient	2-0	0-0	3-1	2-2	1-0	0-0	3-1	3-1	1-0	3-0	3-2	1-1	2-2	2-0	0-0	4-0			3-0	1-0			0-1	1-0
Maidenhead United	0-6	4-3	0-1	1-1	1-0	1-1	2-2	2-0	1-1	1-0	2-0	1-1	3-0	1-3	1-2	0-1	2-1	0-2		3-2	0-3	1-2	1-0	0-2
Maidstone United	1-1	0-2	2-1	1-0	1-2	0-2	0-1	1-1	0-3	0-1	1-3	0-2	0-1	2-3	0-2	1-1	2-0	1-2	2-4		0-2	1-3	0-1	1-1
Salford City	0-1	4-0	0-0	3-1	3-1	2-2	2-1	3-2	1-2	1-3	0-2	1-1	1-1	3-2	3-0	1-1	3-0	1-0	3-0	1-0		2-0	2-0	2-0
Solihull Moors	1-2	1-0	2-2	0-1	0-0	2-1	5-0	2-2	2-0	2-2	4-1	2-1	0-0	1-0	2-0	0-1	3-2	0-0	1-0	5-0	0-0		2-2	1-0
Sutton United	0-0	2-1	0-0	0-1	0-4	0-3	1-0	1-1	1-0	2-2	1-0	1-0	1-1	4-2	2-1	2-2	2-2	1-2	0-1	2-2	2-1	2-2		3-0
Wrexham	0-0	2-0	1-0	1-3	3-0	3-1	2-2	1-0	0-1	0-1	2-0	4-1	0-0	3-1	2-1	1-0	1-0	0-2	1-0	1-0	5-1	1-0	1-0	

National League

Season 2018/2019

Leyton Orient	46	25	14	7	73	35	89
Solihull Moors	46	25	11	10	73	43	86
Salford City	46	25	10	11	77	45	85
Wrexham	46	25	9	12	58	39	84
Fylde	46	22	15	9	72	41	81
Harrogate Town	46	21	11	14	78	57	74
Eastleigh	46	22	8	16	62	63	74
Ebbsfleet United	46	18	13	15	64	50	67
Sutton United	46	17	14	15	55	60	65
Barrow	46	17	13	16	52	51	64
Bromley	46	16	12	18	68	69	60
Barnet	46	16	12	18	45	50	60
Dover Athletic	46	16	12	18	58	64	60
Chesterfield	46	14	17	15	55	53	59
Halifax Town	46	13	20	13	44	43	59
Hartlepool United	46	15	14	17	56	62	59
Gateshead	46	19	9	18	52	48	57
Dagenham & Redbridge	46	15	11	20	50	56	56
Maidenhead United	46	16	6	24	45	70	54
Boreham Wood	46	12	16	18	53	65	52
Aldershot Town	46	11	11	24	38	67	44
Havant & Waterlooville	46	9	13	24	62	84	40
Braintree Town	46	11	8	27	48	78	38
Maidstone United	46	9	7	30	37	82	34

Gateshead had 9 points deducted and were subsequently demoted to the National League North due to financial irregulaties.
As a result Aldershot Town were given a reprieve from relegation. Braintree Town had 3 points deducted for fielding an ineligible player.

National League Promotion Play-offs

AFC Fylde .... 3 Harrogate Town 1
Wrexham .... 0 Eastleigh .... 1 (aet)

Solihull Moors .... 0 AFC Fylde 1
Salford City .... 1 Eastleigh .... 1 (aet)
Salford City won 4-3 on penalties.

AFC Fylde .... 0 Salford City 3

Promoted: Leyton Orient and Salford City

Relegated: Gateshead, Havant & Waterlooville, Braintree Town and Maidstone United

National League North 2018/2019 Season	AFC Telford United	Alfreton Town	Altrincham	Ashton United	Blyth Spartans	Boston United	Brackley Town	Bradford Park Avenue	Chester	Chorley	Curzon Ashton	Darlington	FC United of Manchester	Guiseley	Hereford	Kidderminster Harriers	Leamington	Nuneaton Borough	Southport	Spennymoor Town	Stockport County	York City
AFC Telford United		0-0	1-1	2-1	1-1	1-0	2-1	0-2	3-1	1-1	3-1	3-1	1-3	1-1	1-1	0-1	4-1	3-1	1-0	2-1	1-1	2-1
Alfreton Town	1-1		0-7	2-0	3-1	1-1	0-1	0-1	2-2	2-1	0-1	0-0	2-3	0-1	1-1	3-3	1-2	3-1	3-1	1-7	1-1	2-3
Altrincham	3-1	3-1		3-0	1-1	0-2	1-2	1-1	4-0	5-3	0-2	3-3	1-2	1-1	1-1	2-1	2-2	4-0	1-0	0-2	0-1	3-0
Ashton United	3-4	0-2	1-1		0-3	1-1	1-5	0-2	0-3	0-5	1-2	2-2	1-0	1-0	0-0	0-1	2-1	0-0	1-2	3-0	0-6	0-2
Blyth Spartans	1-0	1-1	2-1	2-0		3-0	1-3	1-2	8-1	1-2	3-2	0-1	0-3	2-0	2-3	3-3	0-2	4-1	2-1	2-2	3-2	2-1
Boston United	2-2	0-1	1-2	2-1	4-0		1-3	2-2	0-2	0-2	4-1	0-2	2-1	1-0	3-1	0-2	1-1	2-1	1-2	0-2	1-3	2-0
Brackley Town	3-1	3-1	1-2	3-1	1-1	2-0		3-0	2-2	2-2	2-0	2-4	1-0	2-0	2-0	3-1	2-2	3-1	2-0	4-1	1-0	0-0
Bradford (Park Avenue)	1-2	1-1	2-3	3-2	1-1	1-0	1-0		2-0	1-0	2-2	2-2	2-3	1-2	1-0	1-2	2-1	1-0	2-2	1-0	1-1	1-3
Chester	2-1	3-2	1-2	4-1	2-0	4-1	0-0	5-3		0-0	0-1	3-1	0-0	1-1	3-0	3-1	1-1	3-2	0-0	0-0	0-6	2-2
Chorley	1-1	3-1	4-1	0-1	2-4	1-1	2-0	3-2	0-0		2-0	3-2	4-0	3-0	1-0	3-0	3-0	2-0	4-0	1-2	2-0	1-0
Curzon Ashton	2-1	3-2	0-6	2-4	1-3	1-3	1-1	1-1	0-3	0-1		1-1	3-1	1-0	0-1	1-1	1-1	0-1	0-3	0-5	2-0	1-0
Darlington	3-0	0-1	0-3	2-1	1-1	1-0	0-2	1-0	0-1	1-1	1-2		2-0	0-0	2-2	3-0	1-1	1-2	0-0	1-2	0-1	5-1
FC United of Manchester	1-2	1-1	1-2	3-4	1-2	0-3	1-1	2-2	0-2	1-4	2-0	1-2		3-3	2-2	0-1	0-2	0-4	1-1	1-3	1-2	3-3
Guiseley	1-1	0-1	2-2	1-1	1-3	4-5	2-1	1-5	1-1	0-2	1-0	1-0	3-0		1-1	0-0	1-1	2-1	0-1	1-1	1-1	1-1
Hereford	1-1	2-1	1-1	0-2	3-0	0-2	0-2	1-2	2-0	1-1	1-2	4-2	1-3	1-0		1-0	2-1	2-2	0-3	0-3	2-2	1-1
Kidderminster Harriers	0-0	0-1	3-2	3-3	3-1	1-2	2-0	3-0	4-1	0-4	1-1	5-2	1-2	1-2	2-1		1-2	4-1	1-4	2-1	2-1	1-2
Leamington	2-2	3-1	3-0	1-0	1-2	2-0	0-0	4-2	1-0	1-1	0-1	2-2	2-2	2-2	2-2	0-4		3-0	1-0	0-2	0-1	0-1
Nuneaton Borough	1-2	1-2	0-2	0-1	1-3	1-5	1-3	0-6	2-3	0-1	2-4	1-2	1-0	1-3	0-0	1-1	0-2		1-4	0-2	0-3	2-2
Southport	0-4	2-1	1-3	2-2	0-1	2-3	0-0	2-2	3-0	5-3	2-2	0-0	0-0	1-0	1-0	2-2	5-1	1-1		1-1	0-1	1-2
Spennymoor Town	2-3	1-1	4-4	5-0	2-2	1-0	2-1	0-2	2-0	1-0	0-0	2-2	2-0	3-2	0-2	2-1	1-0	3-1	1-1		1-3	3-0
Stockport County	3-2	0-1	2-0	2-1	0-1	0-2	1-1	3-0	1-1	3-0	2-0	2-0	5-1	1-1	1-1	1-0	3-1	2-2	3-2	1-0		3-1
York City	1-0	1-2	0-1	2-0	2-0	2-2	2-1	1-4	0-0	1-4	1-1	4-0	2-0	4-2	1-2	0-3	2-2	2-0	1-0	2-3	1-0	

National League North

Season 2018/2019

Stockport County	42	24	10	8	77	36	82
Chorley	42	24	9	9	83	41	81
Brackley Town	42	22	11	9	72	40	77
Spennymoor Town	42	22	10	10	78	48	76
Altrincham	42	20	11	11	85	56	71
Blyth Spartans	42	20	9	13	74	62	69
Bradford Park Avenue	42	18	11	13	71	61	65
AFC Telford United	42	17	14	11	64	55	65
Chester	42	16	14	12	60	62	62
Kidderminster Harriers	42	17	9	16	68	62	60
Boston United	42	17	7	18	62	60	58
York City	42	16	10	16	58	63	58
Leamington	42	13	15	14	57	60	54
Southport	42	13	14	15	58	55	53
Alfreton Town	42	13	12	17	53	67	51
Darlington	42	12	14	16	56	62	50
Hereford	42	11	16	15	47	58	49
Curzon Ashton	42	13	10	19	44	71	49
Guiseley	42	9	17	16	46	60	44
Ashton United	42	9	8	25	43	86	35
FC United of Manchester	42	8	10	24	49	82	34
Nuneaton Borough	42	4	7	31	38	96	19

National League North Promotion Play-offs

Altrincham .... 2 Blyth Spartans .... 2 (aet)
Altrincham won 7-6 on penalties.
Spennymoor Town .... 1 Bradford Park Avenue 0

Chorley .... 1 Altrincham 1
Chorley won 3-1 on penalties.
Brackley Town .... 0 Spennymoor Town .... 0 (aet)
Spennymoor Town won 5-4 on penalties.

Chorley .... 1 Spennymoor Town .... 1 (aet)
Chorley won 4-3 on penalties.

Promoted: Stockport County and Chorley

Relegated: Ashton United, FC United of Manchester and Nuneaton Borough

National League South 2018/2019 Season	Bath City	Billericay Town	Chelmsford City	Chippenham Town	Concord Rangers	Dartford	Dulwich Hamlet	East Thurrock United	Eastbourne Borough	Gloucester City	Hampton & Richmond Borough	Hemel Hempstead Town	Hungerford Town	Oxford City	Slough Town	St. Albans City	Torquay United	Truro City	Wealdstone	Welling United	Weston-super-Mare	Woking
Bath City	■	1-2	2-0	5-0	1-1	1-2	2-1	1-0	1-0	3-0	1-0	0-1	4-1	1-0	2-0	0-3	3-2	1-1	1-1	0-2	2-0	1-1
Billericay Town	0-2	■	0-1	1-2	1-1	1-1	1-1	3-2	2-0	1-0	1-3	2-1	1-2	2-3	3-2	3-2	0-2	3-2	1-0	2-0	4-2	0-4
Chelmsford City	1-0	5-1	■	1-0	2-2	2-1	2-2	1-0	3-2	2-0	2-0	2-1	4-1	2-1	0-1	2-4	0-0	0-2	0-3	0-0	2-2	2-0
Chippenham Town	2-2	2-0	0-1	■	4-1	1-2	1-2	2-0	2-3	1-0	3-2	1-1	3-1	0-1	1-0	0-0	2-1	2-1	3-1	1-4	1-3	2-2
Concord Rangers	2-1	2-2	3-0	1-1	■	2-0	0-0	1-1	3-0	2-0	4-0	2-1	4-0	0-1	2-2	2-1	0-1	3-0	2-2	0-5	3-0	1-1
Dartford	3-0	2-1	1-0	0-1	1-1	■	2-1	2-0	2-2	2-0	2-2	0-0	2-1	3-2	1-1	3-2	0-2	1-1	0-3	1-0	2-1	2-0
Dulwich Hamlet	0-2	2-2	1-3	2-0	0-1	2-0	■	2-1	2-1	0-1	0-2	3-3	3-1	0-1	0-1	1-0	0-2	3-2	1-1	2-1	3-3	1-3
East Thurrock United	1-0	2-1	2-0	2-1	0-2	2-2	0-0	■	0-1	2-0	0-0	1-2	2-1	0-1	1-0	2-4	1-2	2-2	0-1	4-1	2-3	0-1
Eastbourne Borough	0-0	0-2	1-1	2-1	1-2	6-0	2-1	0-2	■	1-2	2-2	3-0	3-1	2-2	2-4	1-2	2-4	2-2	0-3	1-0	1-1	1-2
Gloucester City	0-0	1-4	0-0	3-2	1-2	1-2	1-1	1-0	2-2	■	0-0	1-1	0-0	1-0	1-2	0-0	0-0	0-2	0-0	0-1	1-3	3-4
Hampton & Richmond	0-1	0-2	1-1	2-1	1-4	0-1	2-0	1-0	0-0	0-1	■	1-2	0-3	2-4	1-1	0-1	0-3	2-2	2-1	2-1	3-1	0-3
Hemel Hempstead Town	0-3	0-2	3-5	4-2	2-2	1-2	1-0	3-2	3-2	2-1	1-1	■	0-0	2-1	1-1	1-1	1-4	1-1	0-1	1-1	0-2	0-2
Hungerford Town	0-0	2-2	0-6	2-1	2-1	1-0	1-2	1-1	2-0	1-2	2-0	0-3	■	1-1	1-2	5-0	0-2	1-4	1-1	0-1	0-1	1-1
Oxford City	1-2	2-3	1-3	1-1	2-0	2-1	4-1	3-1	0-0	0-1	3-5	2-1	1-2	■	1-3	2-1	1-0	4-0	3-0	0-1	3-0	1-2
Slough Town	0-0	2-1	1-0	2-2	1-0	2-2	1-2	3-1	1-1	1-2	1-1	1-0	2-0	2-0	■	2-2	0-0	1-2	0-1	1-0	2-1	0-1
St Albans City	0-2	2-1	3-1	2-3	2-0	2-0	1-0	2-1	1-1	1-2	2-3	2-1	3-2	1-0	3-2	■	0-4	2-2	0-0	2-0	2-0	1-1
Torquay United	1-0	2-2	3-1	0-1	4-1	2-0	5-2	2-0	2-0	2-1	0-2	2-0	0-1	7-2	4-0	4-1	■	4-2	3-1	1-2	2-2	
Truro City	1-1	0-4	0-3	1-2	1-3	3-1	3-2	1-3	2-0	1-2	0-2	1-2	2-3	2-0	3-3	2-1	1-3	■	1-2	2-2	3-3	0-1
Wealdstone	3-3	1-1	2-3	1-0	1-1	1-1	1-3	3-0	0-3	2-0	2-1	2-1	1-0	0-2	0-3	2-2	0-3	3-0	■	1-3	4-1	1-0
Welling United	2-1	0-3	2-0	2-1	0-1	2-0	2-0	2-0	1-0	3-1	4-0	1-1	3-1	3-2	2-1	2-2	2-0	5-3	1-1	■	3-1	3-3
Weston-super-Mare	0-2	2-3	0-3	0-1	1-2	3-1	1-1	1-1	0-1	0-0	0-2	1-2	0-0	1-1	2-0	2-3	2-2	1-1	0-5	0-1	■	2-4
Woking	1-3	2-1	1-1	2-0	1-2	0-1	1-2	3-0	2-0	1-2	3-1	3-1	3-0	3-2	0-1	2-1	3-3	3-1	0-2	2-0	2-1	■

National League South

Season 2018/2019

Torquay United	42	27	7	8	93	41	88
Woking	42	23	9	10	76	49	78
Welling United	42	23	7	12	70	47	76
Chelmsford City	42	21	9	12	68	50	72
Bath City	42	20	11	11	58	36	71
Concord Rangers	42	20	13	9	69	48	70
Wealdstone	42	18	12	12	62	50	66
Billericay Town	42	19	8	15	72	65	65
St. Albans City	42	18	10	14	67	64	64
Dartford	42	18	10	14	52	58	64
Slough Town	42	17	12	13	56	50	63
Oxford City	42	17	5	20	64	63	56
Chippenham Town	42	16	7	19	57	64	55
Dulwich Hamlet	42	13	10	19	52	65	49
Hampton & Richmond Borough	42	13	10	19	49	66	49
Hemel Hempstead Town	42	12	12	18	52	67	48
Gloucester City	42	12	11	19	35	54	47
Eastbourne Borough	42	10	12	20	52	65	42
Hungerford Town	42	11	9	22	45	72	42
Truro City	42	9	12	21	63	87	39
East Thurrock United	42	10	7	25	42	63	37
Weston-super-Mare	42	8	11	23	50	80	35

Concord Rangers had 3 points deducted for an infringement of the league's rules and were also barred from entering the play-offs after failing ground size regulations.

National League South Promotion Play-offs

Bath City 1   Wealdstone .... 3 (aet)
Braintree Town won 3-2 on penalties.
Chelmsford City received a bye into the play-off semi-finals.

Woking 3   Wealdstone 2
Welling United 3   Chelmsford City 2

Woking 1   Welling United .... 0 (aet)

Promoted: Torquay United and Woking

Relegated: Truro City, East Thurrock United and Weston-super-Mare

Northern Premier League Premier Division 2018/2019 Season

	Bamber Bridge	Basford United	Buxton	Farsley Celtic	Gainsborough Trinity	Grantham Town	Hednesford Town	Hyde United	Lancaster City	Marine	Matlock Town	Mickleover Sports	Nantwich Town	North Ferriby United	Scarborough Athletic	South Shields	Stafford Rangers	Stalybridge Celtic	Warrington Town	Whitby Town	Witton Albion	Workington
Bamber Bridge		0-4	2-2	0-3	1-2	3-1	1-1	5-2	2-2	1-2	4-2	1-2	2-2		2-4	0-2	6-1	3-0	0-0	1-3	2-0	3-2
Basford United	1-0		2-0	4-3	0-1	3-1	1-2	3-8	3-1	0-0	6-0	2-1	7-3		3-1	0-3	2-2	5-2	2-3	2-0	3-1	3-2
Buxton	0-1	1-0		1-2	1-0	1-0	1-2	1-0	1-2	0-3	2-2	5-0	2-1		1-0	2-0	4-1	1-1	2-2	2-0	0-5	3-2
Farsley Celtic	3-2	2-0	1-1		1-1	1-1	1-2	1-1	2-0	2-0	3-2	1-0	2-1		3-1	4-1	2-1	2-1	3-3	3-1	0-1	2-0
Gainsborough Trinity	2-1	3-2	1-2	0-5		2-3	0-0	1-0	3-1	0-1	4-2	2-0	0-0		0-1	0-1	1-1	1-0	1-4	4-1	1-1	4-1
Grantham Town	1-1	2-1	0-1	0-4	0-2		1-2	1-0	0-2	1-1	2-0	2-1	2-3		1-0	2-1	0-5	0-1	0-2	3-2	1-0	0-2
Hednesford Town	1-1	3-1	1-1	0-1	1-2	2-1		1-0	0-1	0-1	2-0	1-1	4-4		0-1	2-1	1-3	1-0	1-0	1-2	0-1	2-0
Hyde United	0-2	1-0	1-1	1-2	1-3	3-0	2-0		1-2	1-2	1-2	2-1	1-2		2-3	4-1	5-3	1-0	0-2	3-0	1-0	0-0
Lancaster City	1-1	1-1	1-3	2-0	0-1	1-1	2-2	2-1		0-1	1-0	2-2	0-2		0-6	1-1	0-0	1-0	1-3	2-1	1-0	0-2
Marine	0-2	1-4	1-1	1-2	1-1	0-2	3-1	0-0	3-1		1-3	3-0	0-1		1-2	1-3	1-0	1-1	0-2	0-0	2-3	0-2
Matlock Town	2-1	2-2	0-6	1-2	0-2	7-0	3-3	0-0	4-0	3-1		1-1	0-1		0-0	0-3	3-2	3-1	0-2	0-3	1-2	2-1
Mickleover Sports	2-2	0-1	1-3	1-2	0-1	1-3	1-0	0-2	1-1	1-0	0-0		0-0		1-1	1-3	3-2	2-1	1-4	0-1	0-0	1-0
Nantwich Town	2-0	3-2	0-0	2-1	1-0	1-1	2-1	1-1	5-2	3-2	1-4	2-3			1-1	0-0	0-1	4-2	2-1	4-1	0-1	0-0
North Ferriby United																						
Scarborough Athletic	0-0	3-1	4-0	1-3	0-2	2-0	5-3	0-2	1-1	2-0	2-2	0-2	2-3			1-3	4-1	1-2	1-0	1-1	2-0	5-1
South Shields	3-3	1-1	1-1	1-0	1-0	5-0	4-1	4-0	2-0	2-1	5-0	3-2	4-0		3-2		3-0	3-2	1-2	5-2	2-1	4-1
Stafford Rangers	1-0	3-1	0-1	1-3	1-1	1-1	4-1	1-3	1-1	0-0	4-1	1-1	1-4		1-3	1-1		2-0	1-1	3-3	3-1	1-1
Stalybridge Celtic	3-2	0-2	1-1	2-2	2-1	1-0	1-0	2-2	1-2	3-2	3-1	0-0	1-1		2-3	0-1	2-2		1-2	0-1	0-2	1-0
Warrington Town	2-0	1-1	2-1	0-2	2-1	3-0	3-1	2-1	1-1	1-0	0-1	1-0	0-1		2-0	3-0	2-3	0-0		1-0	0-0	2-0
Whitby Town	2-1	4-1	1-0	0-2	1-0	2-1	1-2	0-1	1-1	2-1	1-3	4-0	0-1		2-0	0-1	1-2	2-1	0-1		0-1	0-1
Witton Albion	2-2	2-2	0-3	2-3	0-0	1-0	1-1	1-1	1-0	0-0	1-0	1-2	2-0		2-1	0-1	1-1	1-3	1-2	2-0		2-0
Workington	2-1	0-3	1-1	0-1	0-2	1-4	4-2	1-2	0-2	1-1	3-1	0-1	2-4		2-3	0-2	1-0	1-2	0-2	1-2	0-2	

Evo-Stik League – Northern Premier Division

Season 2018/2019

Farsley Celtic	40	28	6	6	82	40	90
South Shields	40	27	6	7	86	41	87
Warrington Town	40	25	9	6	69	33	84
Nantwich Town	40	19	12	9	70	59	69
Buxton	40	18	12	10	60	45	66
Gainsborough Trinity	40	19	8	13	53	41	65
Basford United	40	18	7	15	82	67	61
Scarborough Athletic	40	18	7	15	70	56	61
Witton Albion	40	16	10	14	45	41	58
Hyde United	40	15	8	17	58	53	53
Whitby Town	40	15	4	21	48	59	49
Lancaster City	40	12	13	15	42	61	49
Hednesford Town	40	13	9	18	51	63	48
Stafford Rangers	40	11	14	15	62	70	47
Matlock Town	40	12	8	20	58	79	44
Bamber Bridge	40	10	12	18	62	67	42
Stalybridge Celtic	40	11	9	20	46	62	42
Grantham Town	40	12	6	22	39	72	42
Mickleover Sports	40	10	11	19	37	61	41
Marine	40	10	10	20	39	54	40
Workington	40	8	5	27	38	73	29

Promotion Play-offs

South Shields .... 4 Buxton 2
Warrington Town .... 4 Nantwich Town 1

South Shields .... 1 Warrington Town 2

Step 3 Super Play-off

Warrington Town .... 2 King's Lynn Town .... 3 (aet)

Promoted: Farsley Celtic

Relegated: Marine and Workington

North Ferriby United folded during the season and their record was expunged.

Southern Football League Premier Division Central 2018/2019 Season	AFC Rushden & Diamonds	Alvechurch	Banbury United	Barwell	Bedworth United	Biggleswade Town	Coalville Town	Halesowen Town	Hitchin Town	Kettering Town	King's Lynn Town	Leiston	Lowestoft Town	Needham Market	Redditch United	Royston Town	Rushall Olympic	St. Ives Town	St. Neots Town	Stourbridge	Stratford Town	Tamworth
AFC Rushden & Diamonds		1-1	1-1	1-1	3-1	3-3	3-1	2-0	2-1	0-1	1-0	1-1	1-1	2-1	5-2	0-0	0-2	0-0	2-0	1-2	2-0	2-2
Alvechurch	0-0		1-1	1-5	3-0	2-1	5-0	1-0	3-1	1-3	0-3	2-1	4-2	3-0	3-0	0-0	1-0	2-1	3-2	0-0	2-2	0-3
Banbury United	1-0	3-1		6-1	1-1	1-2	4-2	2-1	1-2	4-1	2-0	1-0	0-0	2-1	1-1	0-1	2-1	1-2	1-3	0-0	1-1	0-0
Barwell	1-1	1-2	2-1		1-1	0-0	2-3	1-1	0-1	0-1	1-3	3-0	1-1	0-2	4-0	1-2	1-3	1-1	6-1	1-1	0-0	0-1
Bedworth United	1-3	0-2	1-3	0-1		1-4	0-1	0-1	2-2	1-2	0-3	2-2	1-1	0-4	0-2	1-2	1-3	0-2	1-0	0-3	0-2	1-4
Biggleswade Town	1-0	4-2	0-0	1-1	1-1		3-0	1-0	1-1	1-0	1-2	1-2	3-1	2-0	2-0	1-4	0-1	1-0	1-0	1-2	0-0	3-0
Coalville Town	2-2	2-0	1-1	1-0	1-0	2-0		3-0	4-1	2-2	3-3	2-2	1-0	1-2	1-2	2-3	2-2	0-1	1-1	6-4	1-2	1-2
Halesowen Town	0-1	1-1	2-0	0-2	1-3	1-1	1-3		0-0	0-1	2-2	0-0	1-0	1-1	1-0	1-0	2-0	1-1	1-1	0-3	0-2	0-1
Hitchin Town	3-4	1-1	0-1	2-0	4-1	0-2	1-0	5-1		0-1	3-0	2-2	1-3	1-2	1-0	0-2	0-1	1-0	0-2	2-1	2-0	1-0
Kettering Town	2-1	1-2	3-0	0-1	5-1	2-3	2-3	2-0	5-0		2-1	1-2	3-0	3-2	4-4	1-0	2-1	0-3	2-0	4-2	5-1	2-1
King's Lynn Town	1-1	1-0	3-1	3-2	1-1	2-4	4-1	3-0	3-2	0-0		1-1	4-0	1-1	2-0	4-2	3-0	2-0	0-0	1-0	0-0	2-1
Leiston	1-4	2-0	0-0	0-1	1-1	3-0	2-0	4-0	1-2	0-1	1-5		0-4	2-1	4-3	1-1	0-1	0-2	2-0	0-3	1-2	2-2
Lowestoft Town	1-1	1-2	1-0	0-0	3-0	2-1	1-2	5-1	3-2	0-1	1-0	1-2		0-2	0-0	2-0	2-4	0-1	1-2	1-0	3-2	1-3
Needham Market	1-5	1-0	3-3	0-2	4-1	1-0	1-1	1-1	8-1	0-3	1-4	2-2	1-0		3-1	0-2	1-1	4-1	0-1	0-0	2-1	1-3
Redditch United	2-2	4-2	2-0	2-4	0-1	3-3	1-5	3-0	3-1	1-4	1-1	3-1	4-2	4-1		1-2	2-1	2-0	1-1	0-4	0-1	0-0
Royston Town	2-1	0-1	3-0	1-0	2-0	4-6	2-0	0-0	1-0	0-1	0-2	2-5	1-1	2-4	0-1		1-3	1-2	5-0	3-2	2-2	0-2
Rushall Olympic	2-1	1-2	1-1	1-1	0-0	2-2	0-2	0-0	1-2	0-1	2-1	2-0	3-1	0-1	1-3	0-3		4-1	3-2	0-0	2-2	1-1
St. Ives Town	0-0	0-2	2-2	1-2	2-1	0-1	0-1	2-0	2-1	1-2	1-1	0-2	0-1	1-1	1-0	0-0	0-3		0-0	0-0	0-2	1-0
St. Neots Town	0-1	0-3	0-3	1-0	2-1	2-2	1-4	1-1	0-0	0-3	0-5	2-0	1-3	0-3	3-1	1-0	0-1	0-1		1-2	1-2	0-0
Stourbridge	2-1	3-3	2-0	3-0	4-1	2-0	4-2	1-1	3-0	1-2	1-2	4-0	3-1	3-1	4-1	2-1	1-1	1-1	1-0		3-0	1-1
Stratford Town	1-0	0-1	2-1	2-1	3-1	3-2	0-2	2-1	2-0	1-3	0-2	3-2	1-3	3-1	2-0	2-0	0-1	0-0	1-0	0-0		2-1
Tamworth	1-1	1-1	4-0	3-3	2-2	1-1	1-3	4-1	2-0	0-0	0-1	5-0	0-2	1-2	1-3	1-2	2-0	1-2	5-0	1-0	0-1	

Evo-Stik Southern Premier
Premier Division Central

Season 2018/2019

	P	W	D	L	F	A	Pts
Kettering Town	42	30	4	8	84	41	94
King's Lynn Town	42	23	11	8	80	41	80
Stourbridge	42	22	12	8	79	40	78
Alvechurch	42	21	10	11	66	53	73
Stratford Town	42	21	9	12	55	49	72
Coalville Town	42	20	7	15	78	66	67
Biggleswade Town	42	18	12	12	67	54	66
Rushall Olympic	42	17	11	14	56	49	62
AFC Rushden & Diamonds	42	15	16	11	60	49	61
Royston Town	42	18	7	17	59	53	60
Needham Market	42	17	9	16	68	65	60
Tamworth	42	15	13	14	64	46	58
St. Ives Town	42	14	13	15	36	43	55
Lowestoft Town	42	14	9	19	55	60	51
Redditch United	42	14	8	20	63	79	50
Barwell	42	12	13	17	55	55	49
Banbury United	42	13	14	15	53	55	49
Hitchin Town	42	14	6	22	50	71	48
Leiston	42	12	11	19	54	73	47
St. Neots Town	42	9	9	24	32	73	36
Halesowen Town	42	6	14	22	26	66	32
Bedworth United	42	3	10	29	32	91	19

Royston United had one point deducted for fielding an ineligible player.

Banbury United had 4 points deducted for an infringement of the league's rules.

Promotion Play-offs

King's Lynn Town 3   Stratford Town 1
Stourbridge 1   Alvechurch 2

King's Lynn Town 3   Alvechurch 0

Step 3 Super Play-off

Warrington Town 2   King's Lynn Town .... 3 (aet)

Promoted: Kettering Town and King's Lynn Town

Relegated: St. Neots Town, Halesowen Town and Bedworth United

80

Southern Football League Premier Division South 2018/2019 Season	Basingstoke Town	Beaconsfield Town	Chesham United	Dorchester Town	Farnborough	Frome Town	Gosport Borough	Harrow Borough	Hartley Wintney	Hendon	Kings Langley	Merthyr Town	Metropolitan Police	Poole Town	Salisbury	Staines Town	Swindon Supermarine	Taunton Town	Tiverton Town	Walton Casuals	Weymouth	Wimborne Town
Basingstoke Town		2-1	2-3	1-2	1-1	4-1	2-1	2-2	1-3	2-1	3-0	0-3	2-2	1-2	0-2	10-3	2-0	1-2	3-3	2-1	1-2	3-2
Beaconsfield Town	3-2		7-0	2-2	2-6	2-2	4-3	4-1	3-3	0-0	4-2	1-1	0-1	1-1	2-2	3-2	1-0	1-2	0-2	1-1	1-0	2-0
Chesham United	2-1	0-0		0-0	0-1	2-1	1-0	0-4	2-2	2-2	3-0	0-3	1-1	5-1	1-4	7-0	0-0	0-1	1-1	0-2	0-5	1-1
Dorchester Town	4-1	1-3	0-5		0-6	0-1	0-0	3-2	2-1	0-3	2-2	0-0	0-1	0-2	1-4	6-1	0-3	1-2	6-0	1-1	0-1	1-1
Farnborough	2-1	2-0	0-1	2-2		3-2	2-1	4-1	1-1	3-0	0-1	0-1	0-0	1-2	0-3	1-0	2-1	1-4	3-2	1-0	4-3	3-1
Frome Town	1-4	0-1	0-2	0-1	2-3		2-0	1-3	0-1	1-1	1-0	2-3	0-3	1-1	0-0	2-0	1-2	2-0	1-3	3-0	0-2	1-0
Gosport Borough	3-2	2-3	0-0	1-4	0-2	3-1		0-1	1-0	3-1	3-2	0-3	6-3	3-2	1-4	2-1	2-1	1-2	0-1	0-0	0-2	1-0
Harrow Borough	2-1	2-1	0-2	4-1	5-0	1-2	0-1		2-2	3-1	3-4	3-0	4-3	4-0	1-1	9-1	1-3	1-0	2-2	1-1	2-3	0-2
Hartley Wintney	0-2	2-0	1-2	3-1	2-2	2-1	1-0	3-0		2-3	0-0	1-1	1-4	4-3	3-4	7-0	2-2	3-1	1-0	3-4	0-3	3-0
Hendon	1-0	2-2	0-1	0-0	2-1	0-1	0-4	2-4	0-2		1-2	3-0	1-3	1-0	2-2	5-1	1-0	2-3	2-2	3-0	2-3	3-2
Kings Langley	2-0	3-0	1-0	1-0	5-1	2-0	3-0	2-4	2-1	3-1		1-0	1-2	0-3	1-1	3-1	1-2	1-2	2-2	1-0	2-1	1-0
Merthyr Town	1-0	0-1	1-0	1-7	0-0	1-3	4-2	1-1	1-2	0-2	1-1		2-2	0-2	1-2	9-0	2-2	3-1	5-1	1-2	2-1	2-0
Metropolitan Police	4-4	3-1	1-0	2-1	4-3	2-1	2-2	1-0	5-1	3-0	1-0	2-0		1-2	2-2	2-0	0-2	4-1	3-2	2-2	4-4	4-2
Poole Town	3-2	2-1	0-0	0-1	6-0	3-0	1-1	3-3	1-3	0-2	3-0	3-1	2-2		2-2	0-2	2-5	1-0	3-0	3-1	1-1	2-5
Salisbury	2-1	2-1	1-1	3-0	3-2	1-0	0-2	0-6	4-2	3-1	1-2	2-0	1-1	1-2		3-2	2-2	3-2	3-1	4-2	3-4	4-3
Staines Town	0-3	0-1	3-1	1-6	0-3	1-0	0-5	1-5	3-5	2-5	0-2	2-6	0-5	0-7	1-7		2-1	1-3	2-4	1-4	1-4	2-4
Swindon Supermarine	5-2	4-0	0-0	2-0	4-2	0-4	2-1	1-2	1-1	0-1	3-4	3-0	1-0	1-1	2-2	3-0		0-1	0-1	2-1	1-1	3-2
Taunton Town	0-0	2-1	4-0	1-1	2-1	3-0	3-2	7-0	2-2	3-3	2-1	3-2	1-3	1-0	4-3	4-0	1-1		2-1	4-0	3-3	4-2
Tiverton Town	4-1	1-1	0-2	2-3	1-1	3-1	1-0	1-1	1-1	0-0	1-2	2-2	2-1	0-2	2-0	3-2	2-2	1-3		5-1	1-2	0-3
Walton Casuals	3-3	1-1	2-2	2-3	2-1	4-1	3-1	3-2	1-2	5-1	1-0	1-3	2-2	0-4	3-1	3-1	3-1	0-1	1-2		1-2	3-0
Weymouth	1-2	1-1	1-1	5-0	3-0	4-0	1-3	2-2	2-2	3-0	2-2	2-1	4-0	2-2	2-1	4-0	2-1	2-1	2-1	3-2		1-0
Wimborne Town	2-4	0-1	0-0	2-4	1-1	3-2	3-2	5-3	2-1	3-3	5-0	4-0	3-0	0-4	1-4	1-0	1-0	1-1	2-1	3-0	0-0	

Evo-Stik Southern Premier
Premier Division South

Season 2018/2019

	P	W	D	L	F	A	Pts
Weymouth	42	25	11	6	96	51	86
Taunton Town	42	26	7	9	89	56	85
Metropolitan Police	42	22	12	8	91	64	78
Salisbury	42	22	11	9	97	69	77
Poole Town	42	20	10	12	84	59	70
Kings Langley	42	21	6	15	65	61	69
Harrow Borough	42	18	9	15	97	77	63
Hartley Wintney	42	17	12	13	82	70	63
Farnborough	42	18	8	16	72	72	62
Chesham United	42	15	14	13	54	55	59
Swindon Supermarine	42	16	10	16	70	59	58
Beaconsfield Town	42	15	13	14	65	65	58
Merthyr Town	42	15	9	18	68	67	54
Wimborne Town	42	15	7	20	72	75	52
Dorchester Town	42	14	10	18	67	75	52
Hendon	42	14	10	18	64	74	52
Walton Casuals	42	14	9	19	69	78	51
Tiverton Town	42	13	12	17	65	75	51
Gosport Borough	42	15	5	22	63	70	50
Basingstoke Town	42	14	7	21	81	82	49
Frome Town	42	11	4	27	45	74	37
Staines Town	42	4	0	38	40	168	12

Promotion Play-offs

Metropolitan Police 3   Salisbury 2
Taunton Town 1   Poole Town .... 1 (aet)
Poole Town won 4-3 on penalties.

Dulwich Hamlet 1   Hendon .... 1 (aet)
Dulwich Hamlet won 4-3 on penalties

Step 3 Super Play-off

Metropolitan Police 2   Tonbridge Angels .... 3 (aet)

Promoted: Weymouth

Relegated: Basingstoke Town, Frome Town and Staines Town

Isthmian Football League Premier Division 2018/2019 Season	Hornchurch	Bishop's Stortford	Bognor Regis Town	Brightlingsea Regent	Burgess Hill Town	Carshalton Athletic	Corinthian-Casuals	Dorking Wanderers	Enfield Town	Folkestone Invicta	Haringey Borough	Harlow Town	Kingstonian	Leatherhead	Lewes	Margate	Merstham	Potters Bar Town	Tonbridge Angels	Whitehawk	Wingate & Finchley	Worthing
Hornchurch		0-1	1-1	1-2	2-0	1-1	3-0	1-1	2-0	4-1	2-2	3-0	2-2	3-0	1-5	1-2	1-1	0-1	0-2	1-2	3-0	1-1
Bishop's Stortford	1-0		0-0	3-2	2-2	3-1	3-0	1-1	2-1	0-1	2-0	1-0	0-3	1-1	1-2	2-1	2-0	1-2	3-4	4-2	3-2	3-0
Bognor Regis Town	2-0	3-0		1-2	8-0	2-0	0-1	0-1	1-2	2-4	0-4	1-1	3-1	0-4	2-2	0-0	3-1	2-2	2-3	0-0	4-2	2-2
Brightlingsea Regent	1-1	1-0	3-0		3-2	0-2	4-3	0-2	1-0	2-0	0-2	1-1	2-0	1-0	0-0	0-3	1-1	0-1	0-2	3-0	0-1	0-2
Burgess Hill Town	0-3	0-3	0-2	1-1		3-2	2-1	0-0	1-6	0-0	3-1	1-3	0-1	0-3	1-1	0-2	3-0	0-1	0-4	2-4	0-1	2-1
Carshalton Athletic	2-1	2-1	1-1	3-0	2-0		2-3	0-0	1-0	4-2	3-1	2-0	1-1	2-1	2-1	1-2	1-2	1-0	3-0	2-0	5-1	1-2
Corinthian-Casuals	1-0	1-1	1-3	1-1	3-0	1-0		0-0	1-6	1-3	3-1	0-0	1-2	2-1	0-2	0-3	1-1	1-2	2-1	2-0	3-1	1-1
Dorking Wanderers	3-3	1-0	2-0	2-1	6-0	2-3	2-0		1-0	6-0	2-0	5-3	7-1	2-0	1-2	2-0	2-2	4-1	0-1	2-1	3-0	3-0
Enfield Town	2-2	2-1	3-3	0-0	3-1	0-3	0-2	1-1		2-0	2-2	4-1	0-1	0-1	1-1	4-0	0-0	3-1	0-0	6-0	4-1	1-4
Folkestone Invicta	5-0	2-0	1-0	2-3	1-1	2-3	2-1	0-1	2-3		4-0	3-2	2-0	2-0	4-0	1-0	6-2	2-0	0-1	2-1	2-2	0-1
Haringey Borough	3-1	3-1	2-2	2-1	4-4	3-1	2-2	3-2	3-1	1-0		0-2	2-0	0-3	2-1	1-0	2-2	1-0	4-0	3-0	1-2	1-2
Harlow Town	2-4	1-3	1-1	0-1	1-1	0-4	1-2	0-1	1-3	2-4	2-1		3-1	2-2	2-1	3-4	1-4	2-5	1-0	0-3	2-7	0-2
Kingstonian	2-3	3-2	4-1	2-3	2-3	1-1	1-0	0-1	2-1	4-1	0-4	7-0		0-4	2-1	2-1	0-0	1-2	1-1	1-3	1-2	2-3
Leatherhead	1-2	1-0	2-2	0-1	3-0	1-0	1-2	0-3	4-1	0-0	2-1	1-3	2-1		1-1	0-1	0-1	2-1	1-0	1-1	2-1	2-1
Lewes	0-0	1-3	3-3	5-0	0-3	0-1	3-0	0-2	2-2	2-0	0-1	2-1	3-0	1-0		0-0	2-1	0-0	0-0	1-3	4-2	3-4
Margate	0-0	1-4	1-0	1-0	2-3	1-1	5-2	0-1	2-1	0-3	0-1	0-0	1-0	1-1	0-1		1-0	0-2	0-2	1-3	2-2	1-1
Merstham	3-0	1-1	1-2	1-0	0-2	2-0	2-1	4-1	1-0	1-3	0-0	5-1	2-0	0-2	3-2	1-1		3-1	0-3	1-0	3-0	1-0
Potters Bar Town	0-1	4-2	2-2	0-2	0-0	0-1	2-2	0-2	1-2	2-2	0-0	1-2	3-0	0-1	1-0	1-2	0-1		2-1	1-1	4-0	1-1
Tonbridge Angels	1-0	2-3	1-2	2-2	1-0	1-0	2-0	0-2	1-2	1-3	1-0	3-1	3-2	0-2	0-0	1-1	0-1	2-1		2-0	2-1	1-2
Whitehawk	1-1	0-2	1-4	1-1	4-1	2-2	4-0	1-1	1-3	0-0	1-3	4-2	1-1	0-2	0-1	1-0	0-0	0-1	1-0		2-3	1-2
Wingate & Finchley	1-1	2-2	0-2	2-2	4-2	2-0	2-0	1-2	1-1	0-3	0-4	0-2	0-4	1-0	0-1	0-1	2-0	4-2	1-2	1-1		1-2
Worthing	3-1	1-2	0-2	1-1	0-0	3-3	2-0	1-4	0-3	3-2	0-2	9-1	3-1	1-1	3-4	0-1	2-4	1-1	1-1	2-0	2-1	

Isthmian League Premier Division

Season 2018/2019

Dorking Wanderers	42	28	9	5	87	31	93
Carshalton Athletic	42	21	8	13	70	49	71
Haringey Borough	42	21	8	13	73	54	71
Tonbridge Angels	42	21	7	14	59	46	70
Merstham	42	20	10	12	60	50	70
Folkestone Invicta	42	21	6	15	77	58	69
Bishop's Stortford	42	20	7	15	70	57	67
Leatherhead	42	19	8	15	56	42	65
Worthing	42	18	11	13	72	63	65
Enfield Town	42	17	10	15	76	56	61
Lewes	42	16	12	14	61	53	60
Margate	42	16	11	15	45	48	59
Brightlingsea Regent	42	16	11	15	49	54	59
Bognor Regis Town	42	14	15	13	71	62	57
AFC Hornchurch	42	12	14	16	57	59	50
Potters Bar Town	42	13	10	19	51	56	49
Corinthian-Casuals	42	13	8	21	48	74	47
Kingstonian	42	13	6	23	60	78	45
Wingate & Finchley	42	12	7	23	57	86	43
Whitehawk	42	10	11	21	50	72	41
Burgess Hill Town	42	9	10	23	44	91	37
Harlow Town	42	9	7	26	53	107	34

Promotion Play-offs

Carshalton Athletic 1   Merstham 2
Haringey Borough 1   Tonbridge Angels 2

Tonbridge Angels 2   Merstham 0

Step 3 Super Play-off

Metropolitan Police 2   Tonbridge Angels .... 3 (aet)

Promoted: Dorking Wanderers and Tonbridge Angels

Relegated: Whitehawk, Burgess Hill Town and Harlow Town

82

F.A. Trophy 2018/2019

Qualifying 1	AFC Hornchurch	6	Ramsgate	0	
Qualifying 1	AFC Mansfield	1	Hednesford Town	1	
Qualifying 1	AFC Rushden & Diamonds	2	St. Ives Town	1	
Qualifying 1	Alvechurch	1	Stratford Town	1	
Qualifying 1	Ashford Town (Middlesex)	1	Lewes	2	
Qualifying 1	Aveley	1	Dunstable Town	0	
Qualifying 1	Barwell	1	Coalville Town	1	
Qualifying 1	Basingstoke Town	4	Wimborne Town	2	
Qualifying 1	Biggleswade Town	2	Harrow Borough	1	
Qualifying 1	Bracknell Town	2	Bognor Regis Town	2	
Qualifying 1	Brentwood Town	3	Whitstable Town	1	
Qualifying 1	Burgess Hill Town	1	Worthing	1	
Qualifying 1	Buxton	3	King's Lynn Town	3	
Qualifying 1	Cambridge City	1	Basford United	2	
Qualifying 1	Canvey Island	0	Brightlingsea Regent	1	
Qualifying 1	Carlton Town	1	Bedworth United	0	
Qualifying 1	Chipstead	2	Berkhamsted	1	
Qualifying 1	Cinderford Town	2	Street	2	
Qualifying 1	Cleethorpes Town	0	Marske United	2	
Qualifying 1	Didcot Town	1	Mangotsfield United	1	
Qualifying 1	Dorking Wanderers	2	Sevenoaks Town	1	
Qualifying 1	Farnborough	2	Merthyr Town	3	
Qualifying 1	Farsley Celtic	4	Brighouse Town	1	
Qualifying 1	Fleet Town	0	Salisbury	3	
Qualifying 1	Folkestone Invicta	5	Leatherhead	1	
Qualifying 1	Frickley Athletic	0	Ramsbottom United	3	
Qualifying 1	Gainsborough Trinity	0	Tamworth	0	
Qualifying 1	Gosport Borough	1	AFC Totton	2	
Qualifying 1	Grantham Town	0	Halesowen Town	4	
Qualifying 1	Haringey Borough	1	Chesham United	1	
Qualifying 1	Hartley Wintney	1	Tiverton Town	1	
Qualifying 1	Hendon	2	Staines Town	1	
Qualifying 1	Herne Bay	2	Witham Town	1	
Qualifying 1	Hitchin Town	0	Hayes & Yeading United	1	
Qualifying 1	Horsham	3	Corinthian Casuals	0	
Qualifying 1	Hyde United	3	Bamber Bridge	0	
Qualifying 1	Hythe Town	1	Bishop's Stortford	2	
Qualifying 1	Kempston Rovers	1	Beaconsfield Town	1	
Qualifying 1	Kettering Town	2	Stourbridge	0	
Qualifying 1	Kings Langley	0	Needham Market	2	
Qualifying 1	Kingstonian	1	Bedford Town	1	
Qualifying 1	Lowestoft Town	0	Enfield Town	1	
Qualifying 1	Maldon & Tiptree	0	Royston Town	3	
Qualifying 1	Margate	1	Potters Bar Town	2	
Qualifying 1	Marine	0	Lancaster City	2	
Qualifying 1	Merstham	2	East Grinstead Town	0	
Qualifying 1	Metropolitan Police	2	Carshalton Athletic	2	
Qualifying 1	Mickleover Sports	1	Redditch United	0	
Qualifying 1	Mildenhall Town	2	Greenwich Borough	4	(aet)
Qualifying 1	Molesey	0	Walton Casuals	1	
Qualifying 1	Newcastle Town	5	Chasetown	2	
Qualifying 1	Ossett United	2	Clitheroe	1	
Qualifying 1	Pickering Town	2	Droylsden	2	
Qualifying 1	Poole Town	2	Frome Town	1	
Qualifying 1	Sittingbourne	1	Wingate & Finchley	2	
Qualifying 1	South Shields	4	North Ferriby United	0	

Qualifying 1	St. Neots Town	1	Matlock Town	0	
Qualifying 1	Stafford Rangers	2	Rushall Olympic	1	
Qualifying 1	Stalybridge Celtic	1	Nantwich Town	0	
Qualifying 1	Stamford	0	Leek Town	0	
Qualifying 1	Swindon Supermarine	1	Banbury United	1	
Qualifying 1	Taunton Town	1	Weymouth	3	
Qualifying 1	Thame United	4	Bristol Manor Farm	2	
Qualifying 1	Thatcham Town	1	Melksham Town	2	
Qualifying 1	Tonbridge Angels	2	Whyteleafe	1	
Qualifying 1	VCD Athletic	1	Leiston	3	
Qualifying 1	Warrington Town	0	Prescot Cables	1	
Qualifying 1	Whitby Town	0	Witton Albion	1	
Qualifying 1	Whitehawk	2	Harlow Town	3	
Qualifying 1	Wisbech Town	1	Yaxley	1	
Qualifying 1	Workington	1	Scarborough Athletic	0	
Qualifying 1	Yate Town	1	Dorchester Town	1	
Replay	Banbury United	3	Swindon Supermarine	0	
Replay	Beaconsfield Town	3	Kempston Rovers	1	
Replay	Bedford Town	3	Kingstonian	2	
Replay	Bognor Regis Town	2	Bracknell Town	2	(aet)
	Bognor Regis Town won 3-2 on penalties.				
Replay	Carshalton Athletic	2	Metropolitan Police	1	
Replay	Chesham United	2	Haringey Borough	2	(aet)
	Chesham United won 3-1 on penalties.				
Replay	Coalville Town	2	Barwell	3	(aet)
Replay	Dorchester Town	2	Yate Town	0	
Replay	Droylsden	2	Pickering Town	3	
Replay	Hednesford Town	0	AFC Mansfield	1	
Replay	King's Lynn Town	1	Buxton	2	(aet)
Replay	Leek Town	0	Stamford	1	
Replay	Mangotsfield United	2	Didcot Town	4	(aet)
Replay	Stratford Town	3	Alvechurch	0	
Replay	Street	4	Cinderford Town	1	
Replay	Tamworth	3	Gainsborough Trinity	0	
Replay	Tiverton Town	5	Hartley Wintney	1	
Replay	Worthing	2	Burgess Hill Town	1	
Replay	Yaxley	2	Wisbech Town	0	
Qualifying 2	AFC Mansfield	2	Pickering Town	2	
Qualifying 2	Aveley	1	Beaconsfield Town	2	
Qualifying 2	Banbury United	0	Hayes & Yeading United	2	
Qualifying 2	Basford United	4	Stafford Rangers	0	
Qualifying 2	Basingstoke Town	2	Enfield Town	1	
Qualifying 2	Brentwood Town	2	Poole Town	2	
Qualifying 2	Brightlingsea Regent	2	AFC Hornchurch	1	
Qualifying 2	Carshalton Athletic	3	Harlow Town	1	
Qualifying 2	Chipstead	2	Bedford Town	2	
Qualifying 2	Dorchester Town	3	AFC Totton	1	
Qualifying 2	Dorking Wanderers	1	Tonbridge Angels	0	
Qualifying 2	Farsley Celtic	0	Carlton Town	0	
Qualifying 2	Folkestone Invicta	3	Didcot Town	0	
Qualifying 2	Greenwich Borough	1	Bishop's Stortford	0	
Qualifying 2	Halesowen Town	3	Prescot Cables	2	
Qualifying 2	Hendon	1	Biggleswade Town	2	
Qualifying 2	Herne Bay	0	Needham Market	1	
Qualifying 2	Horsham	1	Potters Bar Town	0	
Qualifying 2	Lancaster City	1	Ossett United	0	

Qualifying 2	Leiston	2	Melksham Town	1		
Qualifying 2	Lewes	2	Merthyr Town	0		
Qualifying 2	Marske United	2	Tamworth	0		
Qualifying 2	Newcastle Town	2	Workington	2		
Qualifying 2	Royston Town	5	Thame United	2		
Qualifying 2	Salisbury	2	Merstham	0		
Qualifying 2	South Shields	2	Hyde United	1		
Qualifying 2	St. Neots Town	0	Barwell	1		
Qualifying 2	Stalybridge Celtic	0	Buxton	0		
Qualifying 2	Stamford	1	Kettering Town	0		
Qualifying 2	Stratford Town	1	Mickleover Sports	1		
Qualifying 2	Tiverton Town	2	Wingate & Finchley	3		
Qualifying 2	Walton Casuals	2	Bognor Regis Town	0		
Qualifying 2	Weymouth	2	Street	2		
Qualifying 2	Witton Albion	2	AFC Rushden & Diamonds	0		
Qualifying 2	Worthing	1	Chesham United	0		
Qualifying 2	Yaxley	2	Ramsbottom United	2		
Replay	Bedford Town	2	Chipstead	0		
Replay	Buxton	1	Stalybridge Celtic	2		
Replay	Carlton Town	0	Farsley Celtic	4		
Replay	Mickleover Sports	0	Stratford Town	1		
Replay	Pickering Town	2	AFC Mansfield	0		
Replay	Poole Town	4	Brentwood Town	1		
Replay	Ramsbottom United	5	Yaxley	1		
Replay	Street	0	Weymouth	1		
Replay	Workington	5	Newcastle Town	0		
Round 1	Alfreton Town	0	Farsley Celtic	2		
Round 1	Altrincham	4	Bradford Park Avenue	0		
Round 1	Ashton United	0	Boston United	5		
Round 1	Basford United	2	Curzon Ashton	1		
Round 1	Basingstoke Town	1	Torquay United	1	(aet)
	Torquay United won 5-3 on penalties.					
Round 1	Beaconsfield Town	3	Leiston	1		
Round 1	Bedford Town	2	Worthing	1		
Round 1	Blyth Spartans	4	Marske United	1		
Round 1	Brackley Town	3	Nuneaton Borough	0		
Round 1	Carshalton Athletic	2	Walton Casuals	0		
Round 1	Chippenham Town	1	Wingate & Finchley	1		
Round 1	Concord Rangers	2	Wealdstone	3		
Round 1	Darlington	0	AFC Telford United	2		
Round 1	Dorchester Town	1	Hungerford Town	0		
Round 1	Eastbourne Borough	1	Dartford	1		
Round 1	Gloucester City	1	Biggleswade Town	3		
Round 1	Hampton & Richmond Borough	0	Billericay Town	1		
Round 1	Hayes & Yeading United	0	Brightlingsea Regent	0		
Round 1	Hereford	3	FC United of Manchester	1		
Round 1	Horsham	1	Bath City	2		
Round 1	Kidderminster Harriers	1	York City	3		
Round 1	Lancaster City	2	Guiseley	2		
Round 1	Leamington	2	Witton Albion	1		
Round 1	Lewes	2	Hemel Hempstead Town	2		
Round 1	Oxford City	4	Chelmsford City	0		
Round 1	Pickering Town	0	Ramsbottom United	0		
Round 1	Poole Town	2	Dorking Wanderers	3		
Round 1	Royston Town	1	Needham Market	1		
Round 1	Salisbury	2	East Thurrock United	1		

Round 1	Slough Town	2	Weston-Super-Mare	3	
Round 1	Southport	0	Chester FC	0	
Round 1	Spennymoor Town	8	Halesowen Town	2	
Round 1	Stalybridge Celtic	1	Workington	2	
Round 1	Stamford	1	Barwell	1	
Round 1	Stockport County	3	Chorley	0	
Round 1	Stratford Town	2	South Shields	1	
Round 1	Truro City	3	Greenwich Borough	0	
Round 1	Welling United	1	Dulwich Hamlet	1	
Round 1	Weymouth	1	St. Albans City	1	
Round 1	Woking	2	Folkestone Invicta	0	
Replay	Barwell	3	Stamford	3	(aet)
	Barwell won 7-6 on penalties.				
Replay	Brightlingsea Regent	1	Hayes & Yeading United	2	
Replay	Chester FC	0	Southport	2	
Replay	Dartford	2	Eastbourne Borough	3	
Replay	Dulwich Hamlet	2	Welling United	1	
Replay	Guiseley	1	Lancaster City	2	
Replay	Hemel Hempstead Town	3	Lewes	2	
Replay	Needham Market	2	Royston Town	0	
Replay	Ramsbottom United	2	Pickering Town	1	
Replay	St. Albans City	0	Weymouth	2	
Replay	Wingate & Finchley	3	Chippenham Town	2	
Round 2	AFC Fylde	5	Stratford Town	1	
Round 2	AFC Telford United	4	Farsley Celtic	3	
Round 2	Aldershot Town	3	Bedford Town	3	
Round 2	Altrincham	0	Stockport County	1	
Round 2	Barnet	3	Bath City	2	
Round 2	Barrow	1	FC Halifax Town	2	
Round 2	Biggleswade Town	2	Wealdstone	1	
Round 2	Boreham Wood	3	Torquay United	1	(aet)
Round 2	Brackley Town	4	Hayes & Yeading United	2	
Round 2	Bromley	2	Sutton United	1	
	Bromley were disqualified after it was discovered they had fielded an ineligible player. Sutton United were therefore reinstated and progressed to Round 3.				
Round 2	Carshalton Athletic	1	Dorking Wanderers	0	
Round 2	Chesterfield	5	Basford United	1	
Round 2	Dover Athletic	2	Havant & Waterlooville	2	
Round 2	Eastbourne Borough	0	Dorchester Town	4	
Round 2	Ebbsfleet United	0	Dagenham & Redbridge	1	
Round 2	Harrogate Town	2	York City	1	
Round 2	Hemel Hempstead Town	2	Eastleigh	1	
Round 2	Hereford	2	Billericay Town	1	
Round 2	Lancaster City	0	Blyth Spartans	3	
Round 2	Leamington	0	Hartlepool United	1	
Round 2	Leyton Orient	4	Beaconsfield Town	0	
Round 2	Maidenhead United	1	Oxford City	2	(aet)
Round 2	Salford City	3	Gateshead	1	
Round 2	Salisbury	2	Braintree Town	1	
Round 2	Southport	0	Solihull Moors	1	
Round 2	Spennymoor Town	4	Barwell	0	
Round 2	Truro City	4	Weston-Super-Mare	0	
Round 2	Weymouth	w/o	Needham Market		
	Needham Market withdrew from the competition.				
Round 2	Wingate & Finchley	2	Dulwich Hamlet	0	
Round 2	Woking	1	Maidstone United	1	

Round 2	Workington	0	Ramsbottom United	0	
Round 2	Wrexham	3	Boston United	0	
Replay	Bedford Town	7	Aldershot Town	0	
Replay	Havant & Waterlooville	0	Dover Athletic	1	
Replay	Maidstone United	3	Woking	2	(aet)
Replay	Ramsbottom United	2	Workington	0	
Round 3	AFC Fylde	1	Biggleswade Town	0	
Round 3	Barnet	2	Dorchester Town	1	
Round 3	Blyth Spartans	1	Boreham Wood	0	
Round 3	Carshalton Athletic	4	Salisbury	1	
Round 3	Chesterfield	1	Bedford Town	0	
Round 3	Dover Athletic	1	Harrogate Town	2	
Round 3	FC Halifax Town	2	Solihull Moors	2	
Round 3	Hartlepool United	1	AFC Telford United	2	
Round 3	Hemel Hempstead Town	4	Wingate & Finchley	2	
Round 3	Hereford	1	Brackley Town	3	
Round 3	Maidstone United	1	Oxford City	0	
Round 3	Ramsbottom United	2	Weymouth	2	
Round 3	Salford City	2	Dagenham & Redbridge	0	
Round 3	Spennymoor Town	3	Sutton United	0	
Round 3	Stockport County	5	Truro City	0	
Round 3	Wrexham	0	Leyton Orient	1	
Replay	Solihull Moors	1	FC Halifax Town	0	
Replay	Weymouth	1	Ramsbottom United	3	
Round 4	Carshalton Athletic	3	Barnet	3	
Round 4	Chesterfield	0	Brackley Town	2	
Round 4	Harrogate Town	2	Stockport County	4	
Round 4	Hemel Hempstead Town	0	Solihull Moors	5	
Round 4	Leyton Orient	1	Blyth Spartans	0	
Round 4	Ramsbottom United	5	AFC Fylde	5	
Round 4	Salford City	1	Maidstone United	1	
Round 4	Spennymoor Town	1	AFC Telford United	2	
Replay	AFC Fylde	4	Ramsbottom United	1	
Replay	Barnet	2	Carshalton Athletic	1	
Replay	Maidstone United	3	Salford City	0	
Round 5	AFC Fylde	0	Barnet	0	(aet)
	AFC Fylde won 4-1 on penalties.				
Round 5	Brackley Town	1	Leyton Orient	2	
Round 5	Solihull Moors	1	AFC Telford United	2	
Round 5	Stockport County	1	Maidstone United	1	
Replay	Maidstone United	0	Stockport County	3	

Semi-finals

1st leg	AFC Telford United	1	Leyton Orient	2	
1st leg	AFC Fylde	0	Stockport County	0	
2nd leg	Leyton Orient	1	AFC Telford United	0	
	Leyton Orient won 3-1 on aggregate.				
2nd leg	Stockport County	2	AFC Fylde	3	
	AFC Fylde won 3-2 on aggregate.				
FINAL	AFC Fylde	1	Leyton Orient	0	

F.A. Vase 2018/2019

Round 1	1874 Northwich	5	Cammell Laird 1907	0	
Round 1	AFC Croydon Athletic	3	Fareham Town	0	
Round 1	AFC St Austell	6	Plymouth Parkway	1	
Round 1	Almondsbury	2	Bitton	1	
Round 1	Alresford Town	1	Abingdon United	0	
Round 1	Andover Town	1	Badshot Lea	4	
Round 1	Aylestone Park	0	Blidworth Welfare	3	
Round 1	Baldock Town	3	Brimsdown	0	
Round 1	Barrow Town	0	Dronfield Town	1	
Round 1	Barton Town	8	Brandon United	0	
Round 1	Bashley	1	Baffins Milton Rovers	2	
Round 1	Bearsted	3	Beckenham Town	0	
Round 1	Bedfont & Feltham	1	Erith Town	2	
Round 1	Bedlington Terriers	5	Whickham	1	
Round 1	Belper United	1	Quorn	4	
Round 1	Biggleswade United	2	Holbeach United	3	(aet)
Round 1	Billingham Town	1	Dunston UTS	3	
Round 1	Bishop Auckland	2	Hemsworth MW	3	
Round 1	Bodmin Town	2	AFC Stoneham	1	
Round 1	Boldmere St Michaels	2	Rugby Town	1	
Round 1	Bournemouth (Amateurs)	6	Newquay	0	
Round 1	Bridport	0	Falmouth Town	6	
Round 1	Brimscombe & Thrupp	2	Cribbs	3	
Round 1	Broadfields United	1	Banstead Athletic	7	
Round 1	Brocton	3	Highgate United	2	(aet)
Round 1	Buckingham Athletic	2	FC Clacton	2	(aet)
Round 1	Bustleholme	1	NKF Burbage	4	
Round 1	Cadbury Athletic	4	Hanley Town	0	
Round 1	Cadbury Heath	5	Sidmouth Town	0	
Round 1	Canterbury City	2	Saltdean United	1	
Round 1	Cheddar	1	Totton & Eling	0	(aet)
Round 1	Chertsey Town	6	Flackwell Heath	1	
Round 1	Codicote	1	Wantage Town	7	
Round 1	Colney Heath	1	Histon	1	(aet)
Round 1	Corinthian	3	Deal Town	2	
Round 1	Coventry United	5	Wednesfield	0	
Round 1	Eastwood Community	3	Selston	0	
Round 1	Enfield Borough	2	Kirkley & Pakefield	3	(aet)
Round 1	Eversley & California	0	Horndean	1	
Round 1	Exmouth Town	2	Elburton Villa	0	
Round 1	FC Deportivo Galicia	1	Irchester United	2	
Round 1	Great Yarmouth Town	3	Wroxham	1	
Round 1	Hallam	3	Charnock Richard	1	
Round 1	Hanworth Villa	2	Pagham	4	
Round 1	Harefield United	0	Woodbridge Town	2	
Round 1	Haverhill Borough	3	Swaffham Town	4	
Round 1	Heanor Town	0	Ilkeston Town	3	
Round 1	Hebburn Town	4	City of Liverpool	0	
Round 1	Hereford Lads Club	2	Paget Rangers	0	
Round 1	Horsham YMCA	0	Kensington Borough	2	
Round 1	Hucknall Town	3	Black Country Rangers	2	
Round 1	Irlam	2	Handsworth Parramore	0	
Round 1	Ivybridge Town	0	Holyport	0	(aet)
Round 1	Leverstock Green	3	Sawbridgeworth Town	0	
Round 1	Litherland Remyca	1	Thackley	4	
Round 1	Little Oakley	2	Enfield 1893	2	(aet)

Round 1	London Colney	2	Wellingborough Town	3	(aet)
Round 1	Longlevens	1	Tavistock	3	(aet)
Round 1	Longwell Green Sports	1	Brockenhurst	3	
Round 1	Loughborough University	1	Heather St Johns	2	
Round 1	Lye Town	5	Chelmsley Town	2	
Round 1	May & Baker Eastbrook Community	4	North Greenford United	2	(aet)
Round 1	Nelson	0	Ashington	5	
Round 1	Newbury Forest	2	Newport Pagnell Town	3	
Round 1	Newhaven	2	Rusthall	1	
Round 1	Newmarket Town	0	Deeping Rangers	1	
Round 1	Odd Down	1	Willand Rovers	4	
Round 1	Prestwich Heys	6	Garforth Town	2	
Round 1	Rayners Lane	2	Abbey Rangers	3	
Round 1	Redhill	2	Peacehaven & Telscombe	3	
Round 1	Roman Glass St George	0	Malmesbury Victoria	2	
Round 1	Romulus	3	Wellington AFC	3	(aet)
Round 1	Runcorn Town	3	Guisborough Town	3	(aet)
Round 1	Saffron Dynamo	3	Bottesford Town	3	(aet)
Round 1	Saltash United	2	Westbury United	1	
Round 1	Shaftesbury	1	Hamworthy United	2	
Round 1	Sheppey United	4	East Preston	0	
Round 1	Shepshed Dynamo	2	Bewdley Town	0	
Round 1	Shildon	1	Glasshoughton Welfare	0	
Round 1	Sidlesham	0	Chatham Town	2	
Round 1	Sleaford Town	2	Peterborough Northern Star	2	(aet)
Round 1	Smethwick	0	Walsall Wood	3	
Round 1	Southall	6	Sheerwater	0	
Round 1	Southend Manor	1	Redbridge	4	
Round 1	Spelthorne Sports	2	CB Hounslow United	1	
Round 1	Sporting Khalsa	1	Winsford United	0	
Round 1	Squires Gate	2	Sandbach United	1	
Round 1	St Panteleimon	1	Cray Valley Paper Mills	3	
Round 1	Staveley MW	2	Silsden	2	(aet)
Round 1	Steeton	2	Avro	3	
Round 1	Steyning Town Community	1	Walton & Hersham	0	
Round 1	Stowmarket Town	5	Harpenden Town	0	
Round 1	Sunderland RCA	3	Bridlington Town	2	(aet)
Round 1	Sutton Common Rovers	2	Cobham	1	
Round 1	Swallownest	1	Garstang	1	(aet)
	Garstang won 4-3 on penalties.				
Round 1	Takeley	0	Wodson Park	2	
Round 1	Thame Rangers	4	Crawley Green	2	
Round 1	Torpoint Athletic	0	Sholing	1	
Round 1	Tunbridge Wells	0	AFC Uckfield Town	2	
Round 1	Vauxhall Motors	4	Seaham Red Star	0	
Round 1	Wellington Amateurs	1	Leicester Nirvana	2	
Round 1	West Essex	1	Godmanchester Rovers	2	
Round 1	Wick	0	Lordswood	3	
Round 1	Winterton Rangers	1	Lower Breck	0	
Round 1	Worcester City	2	Long Eaton United	1	
Replay	Bottesford Town	2	Saffron Dynamo	3	
Replay	Enfield 1893	2	Little Oakley	0	
Replay	FC Clacton	3	Buckingham Athletic	2	
Replay	Guisborough Town	2	Runcorn Town	4	(aet)
Replay	Histon	2	Colney Heath	0	

Replay	Holyport	0	Ivybridge Town	3	
Replay	Peterborough Northern Star	2	Sleaford Town	0	
Replay	Silsden	2	Staveley MW	0	
Replay	Wellington AFC	1	Romulus	3	
Round 2	AFC Croydon Athletic	1	AFC Uckfield Town	2	
Round 2	Abbey Rangers	5	Lordswood	0	
Round 2	Almondsbury	1	Hamble ASSC	2	
Round 2	Avro	2	Squires Gate	1	
Round 2	Badshot Lea	0	Cray Valley Paper Mills	7	
Round 2	Baffins Milton Rovers	3	Bournemouth (Amateurs)	2	
Round 2	Barton Town	0	Shildon	2	
Round 2	Bearsted	1	Newhaven	0	
Round 2	Biggleswade	3	Norwich CBS	1	
Round 2	Bodmin Town	1	Alresford Town	0	(aet)
Round 2	Brockenhurst	0	Bradford Town	4	
Round 2	Cadbury Athletic	3	Heather St Johns	2	
Round 2	Cheddar	1	AFC St Austell	2	
Round 2	Chertsey Town	2	Horndean	0	
Round 2	Chichester City	0	Windsor	2	
Round 2	Cogenhoe United	2	Leighton Town	0	

Cogenhoe United were disqualified after it was discovered they had fielded an ineligible player. Leighton Town were therefore reinstated and progressed to Round 3.

Round 2	Corinthian	2	Canterbury City	4	(aet)
Round 2	Coventry United	3	Boldmere St Michaels	0	
Round 2	Crowborough Athletic	0	Eastbourne Town	4	
Round 2	Enfield 1893	1	Leverstock Green	4	
Round 2	Exmouth Town	3	Cadbury Heath	4	
Round 2	FC Clacton	1	Kirkley & Pakefield	0	
Round 2	Garstang	2	Sunderland RCA	6	
Round 2	Great Yarmouth Town	1	Godmanchester Rovers	3	
Round 2	Hallam	1	Hebburn Town	2	
Round 2	Hamworthy United	3	Falmouth Town	1	(aet)
Round 2	Hinckley	3	Hereford Lads Club	1	
Round 2	Histon	5	Woodbridge Town	4	
Round 2	Hullbridge Sports	3	Irchester United	1	
Round 2	Irlam	3	Hemsworth MW	1	
Round 2	Ivybridge Town	1	Saltash United	3	
Round 2	Kensington Borough	0	Erith Town	3	
Round 2	Leicester Nirvana	3	Saffron Dynamo	0	
Round 2	Lye Town	4	Brocton	1	
Round 2	May & Baker Eastbrook Community	0	Swaffham Town	1	
Round 2	Newcastle Benfield	2	1874 Northwich	0	
Round 2	Newport (IOW)	0	Cribbs	2	
Round 2	Newport Pagnell Town	3	Thame Rangers	2	
Round 2	Pagham	4	Peacehaven & Telscombe	1	
Round 2	Prestwich Heys	0	1874 Northwich	0	(aet)
Round 2	Quorn	1	Eastwood Community	2	
Round 2	Redbridge	1	Peterborough Northern Star	0	
Round 2	Shepshed Dynamo	3	Blidworth Welfare	0	
Round 2	Sholing	5	Malmesbury Victoria	1	
Round 2	Silsden	3	Bedlington Terriers	1	
Round 2	Southall	1	Chatham Town	0	(aet)
Round 2	Spelthorne Sports	1	Sheppey United	2	
Round 2	Sporting Khalsa	3	Hucknall Town	2	
Round 2	Steyning Town Community	1	Banstead Athletic	0	

Round 2	Stockton Town	4	Ashington	1	
Round 2	Stourport Swifts	0	NKF Burbage	2	
Round 2	Stowmarket Town	3	Baldock Town	1	(aet)
Round 2	Sutton Common Rovers	6	Horley Town	1	
Round 2	Thackley	0	West Auckland Town	1	
Round 2	Vauxhall Motors	1	Runcorn Town	3	
Round 2	Walsall Wood	3	Dronfield Town	1	
Round 2	Wantage Town	1	Deeping Rangers	2	
Round 2	Wellingborough Town	0	Tring Athletic	7	
Round 2	Westfields	3	Romulus	2	
Round 2	Willand Rovers	2	Tavistock	1	
Round 2	Winterton Rangers	2	Dunston UTS	1	
Round 2	Wodson Park	0	Holbeach United	2	
Round 2	Wolverhampton Sporting Community	0	Ilkeston Town	2	
Round 2	Worcester City	0	Desborough Town	2	
Replay	1874 Northwich	1	Prestwich Heys	0	
Round 3	1874 Northwich	3	Silsden	0	
Round 3	AFC Uckfield Town	5	Sutton Common Rovers	2	
Round 3	Avro	0	West Auckland Town	2	
Round 3	Bearsted	3	Steyning Town Community	2	(aet)
Round 3	Bradford Town	1	Baffins Milton Rovers	3	
Round 3	Cadbury Athletic	3	Desborough Town	2	
Round 3	Cadbury Heath	4	AFC St Austell	8	
Round 3	Canterbury City	1	Southall	0	(aet)
Round 3	Coventry United	4	Hinckley	0	
Round 3	Deeping Rangers	4	FC Clacton	2	
Round 3	Eastbourne Town	0	Abbey Rangers	1	
Round 3	Erith Town	1	Windsor	2	
Round 3	Godmanchester Rovers	2	Holbeach United	0	
Round 3	Hamble ASSC	1	Hamworthy United	1	(aet)
Round 3	Histon	5	Leverstock Green	1	
Round 3	Hullbridge Sports	0	Newport Pagnell Town	2	
Round 3	Ilkeston Town	1	Eastwood Community	2	
Round 3	Lye Town	4	Leighton Town	0	(aet)
Round 3	Newcastle Benfield	5	Runcorn Town	4	
Round 3	Redbridge	0	Chertsey Town	5	
Round 3	Saltash United	2	Cribbs	4	
Round 3	Sheppey United	0	Cray Valley Paper Mills	4	
Round 3	Shepshed Dynamo	3	NKF Burbage	0	
Round 3	Shildon	2	Sunderland RCA	3	
Round 3	Sholing	6	Pagham	2	
Round 3	Sporting Khalsa	3	Walsall Wood	1	
Round 3	Stockton Town	3	Hebburn Town	5	
Round 3	Swaffham Town	0	Stowmarket Town	0	(aet)
Round 3	Tring Athletic	1	Biggleswade	1	(aet)
Round 3	Westfields	0	Leicester Nirvana	4	
Round 3	Willand Rovers	3	Bodmin Town	0	
Round 3	Winterton Rangers	2	Irlam	0	
Replay	Biggleswade	0	Tring Athletic	0	(aet)
	Biggleswade won 5-3 on penalties.				
Replay	Hamworthy United	4	Hamble ASSC	1	
Replay	Stowmarket Town	2	Swaffham Town	1	

Round 4	AFC Uckfield Town	1	Windsor	4	
Round 4	Bearsted	1	Abbey Rangers	2	(aet)
Round 4	Biggleswade	1	Stowmarket Town	0	
Round 4	Canterbury City	3	Newport Pagnell Town	2	
Round 4	Chertsey Town	5	AFC St Austell	0	
Round 4	Coventry United	3	Leicester Nirvana	2	

Coventry United were disqualified after it was discovered they had fielded an ineligible player. Leicester Nirvana were therefore reinstated and progressed to Round 5.

Round 4	Cray Valley Paper Mills	3	Baffins Milton Rovers	1	
Round 4	Cribbs	0	Sholing	2	
Round 4	Deeping Rangers	4	Eastwood Community	0	
Round 4	Godmanchester Rovers	1	Sporting Khalsa	0	

Godmanchester Rovers were disqualified after it was discovered they had fielded an ineligible player. Sporting Khalsa were therefore reinstated and progressed to Round 5.

Round 4	Hebburn Town	2	Shepshed Dynamo	1	
Round 4	Histon	2	Lye Town	1	
Round 4	Irlam	4	Cadbury Athletic	0	
Round 4	Newcastle Benfield	2	1874 Northwich	3	
Round 4	Sunderland RCA	0	West Auckland Town	1	
Round 4	Willand Rovers	1	Hamworthy United	0	
Round 5	Biggleswade	6	Windsor	1	
Round 5	Canterbury City	2	Leicester Nirvana	1	
Round 5	Cray Valley Paper Mills	3	Abbey Rangers	1	
Round 5	Hebburn Town	0	West Auckland Town	2	
Round 5	Histon	1	1874 Northwich	3	(aet)
Round 5	Irlam	0	Chertsey Town	2	
Round 5	Sholing	3	Sporting Khalsa	1	
Round 5	Willand Rovers	3	Deeping Rangers	2	
Round 6	1874 Northwich	3	Sholing	1	(aet)
Round 6	Canterbury City	2	Biggleswade	1	
Round 6	West Auckland Town	0	Chertsey Town	2	
Round 6	Willand Rovers	1	Cray Valley Paper Mills	3	

Semi-finals
1st leg	Canterbury City	1	Cray Valley Paper Mills	1	
1st leg	1874 Northwich	1	Chertsey Town	1	
2nd leg	Chertsey Town	0	1874 Northwich	0	(aet)

Aggregate 1-1. Chertsey Town won 5-3 on penalties.
| 2nd leg | Cray Valley Paper Mills | 1 | Canterbury City | 0 | |

Cray Valley Paper Mills won 2-1 on aggregate.

| FINAL | Chertsey Town | 3 | Cray Valley Paper Mills | 1 | (aet) |

National League Fixtures 2019/2020 Season	AFC Fylde	Aldershot Town	Barnet	Barrow	Boreham Wood	Bromley	Chesterfield	Chorley	Dagenham & Redbridge	Dover Athletic	Eastleigh	Ebbsfleet United	FC Halifax Town	Harrogate Town	Hartlepool United	Maidenhead United	Notts County	Solihull Moors	Stockport County	Sutton United	Torquay United	Woking	Wrexham	Yeovil Town
AFC Fylde		14/03	07/09	01/01	01/02	25/04	08/10	06/08	23/11	02/11	21/09	10/08	13/04	26/08	28/03	15/02	30/11	07/03	28/12	12/10	18/01	17/08	24/09	21/12
Aldershot Town	03/08		28/12	07/09	15/02	13/08	30/11	18/01	07/03	08/10	01/01	25/04	17/08	01/02	12/10	02/11	23/11	04/04	21/12	26/08	13/04	21/03	21/09	24/09
Barnet	07/12	03/09		29/02	26/12	08/10	17/08	02/11	18/01	13/08	25/04	26/11	04/01	15/02	01/02	14/09	04/04	28/09	16/11	21/03	26/08	12/10	13/04	03/08
Barrow	26/12	07/12	23/11		08/10	18/01	13/04	26/11	15/02	12/10	10/08	04/01	26/08	06/08	03/09	28/09	07/03	14/09	28/03	02/11	01/02	25/04	14/03	17/08
Boreham Wood	26/10	29/10	01/01	25/01		13/04	10/08	25/04	28/03	07/09	28/12	26/08	08/02	21/12	29/02	16/11	24/09	05/10	21/09	17/08	14/03	30/11	06/08	22/02
Bromley	31/08	28/03	25/01	05/10	24/08		07/09	14/03	28/12	01/01	21/12	06/08	26/10	16/11	18/04	10/04	21/09	08/02	29/10	29/02	10/08	24/09	22/02	30/11
Chesterfield	25/01	28/09	18/04	24/08	04/04	07/12		16/11	31/08	03/08	05/10	22/02	03/09	29/02	26/11	21/03	26/10	26/12	10/04	04/01	14/09	13/08	08/02	29/10
Chorley	21/03	05/10	22/02	24/09	31/08	03/08	07/03		30/11	21/12	08/02	29/10	25/01	28/12	24/08	18/04	10/04	13/08	07/09	09/04	23/11	21/09	01/01	26/10
Dagenham & Red.	29/02	16/11	05/10	29/10	13/08	04/09	25/04	28/09		21/03	13/04	26/12	04/04	17/08	14/09	07/12	25/01	22/02	08/02	26/11	01/04	03/08	26/10	26/08
Dover Athletic	22/02	25/01	28/03	08/02	07/12	26/12	14/03	14/09	06/08		29/10	03/09	28/09	25/04	04/01	26/11	05/10	23/11	26/10	13/04	17/08	26/08	10/08	07/03
Eastleigh	04/01	26/12	31/08	04/04	03/09	14/09	18/01	12/10	24/08	15/02		07/12	29/02	02/11	28/09	08/10	03/08	10/04	18/04	13/08	26/11	01/02	16/11	21/03
Ebbsfleet United	04/04	31/08	24/09	21/09	10/04	21/03	02/11	15/02	01/01	28/12	07/09		03/08	18/01	16/11	12/10	24/08	18/04	29/02	01/02	08/10	21/12	30/11	13/08
FC Halifax Town	24/08	18/04	21/09	10/04	12/10	01/02	28/12	08/10	10/08	30/11	23/11	14/03		24/09	06/08	18/01	21/12	31/08	01/01	15/02	02/11	07/03	28/03	07/09
Harrogate Town	10/04	26/10	29/10	21/03	14/09	07/03	23/11	03/09	18/04	31/08	22/02	05/10	26/11		26/12	04/01	13/08	03/08	24/08	28/09	07/12	04/04	25/01	08/02
Hartlepool United	13/08	08/02	26/10	28/12	23/11	17/08	24/09	13/04	21/12	21/09	30/11	07/03	21/03	01/01		04/04	22/02	29/10	25/01	03/08	25/04	07/09	26/08	05/10
Maidenhead United	29/10	22/02	21/12	30/11	07/03	26/08	06/08	17/08	07/09	24/09	25/01	08/02	05/10	21/09	10/08		01/01	26/10	14/03	25/04	28/03	23/11	28/12	13/04
Notts County	28/09	29/02	10/08	16/11	26/11	04/01	01/02	26/08	08/10	18/01	14/03	13/04	14/09	28/03	02/11	26/12		03/09	06/08	07/12	12/10	15/02	18/08	25/04
Solihull Moors	16/11	10/08	30/11	21/12	18/01	12/10	01/01	28/03	02/11	29/02	26/08	17/08	25/04	14/03	15/02	01/02	28/12		24/09	08/10	06/08	13/04	07/09	21/09
Stockport County	03/09	14/09	07/03	13/08	04/01	15/02	26/08	07/12	12/10	01/02	17/08	23/11	26/12	13/04	04/09	10/08	03/08	21/03		18/01	28/09	02/11	25/04	04/04
Sutton United	08/02	10/04	06/08	22/02	18/04	23/11	21/09	10/08	24/09	24/08	28/03	26/10	29/10	30/11	14/03	31/08	07/09	25/01	05/10		07/03	01/01	21/12	28/12
Torquay United	05/10	24/08	10/04	26/10	03/08	04/04	21/12	29/02	21/09	18/04	24/09	25/01	22/02	07/09	31/08	13/08	08/02	21/03	30/11	16/11		28/12	29/10	01/01
Woking	18/04	06/08	08/02	31/08	28/09	26/11	28/03	04/01	14/03	10/04	26/10	14/09	16/11	10/08	07/12	29/02	29/10	24/08	22/02	26/12	03/09		05/10	25/01
Wrexham	26/11	04/01	24/08	03/08	21/03	02/11	12/10	26/12	01/02	04/04	07/03	28/09	13/08	08/10	10/04	03/09	18/04	07/12	31/08	14/09	15/02	18/01		23/11
Yeovil Town	14/09	26/11	14/03	18/04	02/11	28/09	15/02	01/02	10/04	16/11	06/08	28/03	07/12	12/10	18/01	24/08	31/08	04/01	10/08	03/09	26/12	08/10	29/02	

Please note that the above fixtures may be subject to change.

National League North Fixtures 2019/2020 Season	AFC Telford United	Alfreton Town	Altrincham	Blyth Spartans	Boston United	Brackley Town	Bradford Park Avenue	Chester	Curzon Ashton	Darlington	Farsley Celtic	Gateshead	Gloucester City	Guiseley	Hereford	Kettering Town	Kidderminster Harriers	King's Lynn Town	Leamington	Southport	Spennymoor Town	York City
AFC Telford United	■	26/12	01/02	18/01	02/11	04/01	25/04	14/09	15/02	07/03	07/12	10/08	03/09	19/10	28/03	14/03	06/08	17/08	26/08	13/04	16/11	12/10
Alfreton Town	01/01	■	28/03	10/08	06/08	14/03	17/08	15/02	07/09	28/09	19/10	25/01	16/11	13/04	01/02	21/12	25/04	28/12	11/01	26/08	02/11	07/03
Altrincham	26/10	13/08	■	09/11	10/04	18/04	25/01	21/03	01/01	24/08	31/08	28/09	04/04	11/01	16/11	08/02	21/12	22/02	07/09	28/12	07/03	03/08
Blyth Spartans	28/09	04/04	15/02	■	01/02	30/11	13/04	19/10	11/01	28/12	02/11	01/01	03/08	26/08	17/08	29/02	07/09	25/01	25/04	21/12	21/03	13/08
Boston United	22/02	21/03	26/08	26/10	■	09/11	07/09	03/08	30/11	11/01	29/02	21/12	13/04	17/08	25/04	28/12	25/01	01/01	13/08	28/09	04/04	08/02
Brackley Town	07/09	03/08	17/08	07/03	15/02	■	28/09	02/11	21/12	16/11	01/02	25/04	26/08	25/01	13/04	01/01	28/12	13/08	21/03	11/01	19/10	04/04
Bradford Park Avenue	31/08	18/04	07/12	24/08	04/01	18/01	■	07/03	14/03	10/04	03/09	28/03	08/02	06/08	12/10	22/02	10/08	09/11	16/11	26/10	14/09	26/12
Chester	21/12	09/11	06/08	08/02	14/03	22/02	30/11	■	28/12	25/01	10/08	29/02	17/08	07/09	26/08	28/03	13/04	11/01	28/09	01/01	25/04	26/10
Curzon Ashton	09/11	04/01	26/12	12/10	07/03	14/09	03/08	02/09	■	12/08	18/01	08/02	22/02	25/04	07/12	26/10	17/08	13/04	04/04	21/03	26/08	16/11
Darlington	30/11	18/01	13/04	04/09	12/10	29/02	26/08	07/12	28/03	■	14/03	07/08	04/01	01/02	02/11	10/08	19/10	25/04	15/02	17/08	26/12	14/09
Farsley Celtic	25/01	08/02	25/04	22/02	16/11	26/10	28/12	04/04	28/09	03/08	■	13/04	09/11	01/01	07/03	07/09	11/01	26/08	21/12	13/08	17/08	21/03
Gateshead	04/04	07/12	18/01	26/12	14/09	31/08	13/08	16/11	19/10	21/03	24/08	■	12/10	02/11	04/01	18/04	15/02	07/03	01/02	03/08	03/09	10/04
Gloucester City	28/12	29/02	10/08	14/03	24/08	10/04	19/10	18/04	02/11	07/09	15/02	11/01	■	28/09	06/08	30/11	28/03	21/12	01/01	25/01	01/02	31/08
Guiseley	08/02	24/08	12/10	10/04	18/04	07/12	21/03	04/01	31/08	26/10	26/12	22/02	18/01	■	14/09	09/11	16/11	03/08	07/03	04/04	13/08	03/09
Hereford	13/08	26/10	29/02	18/04	31/08	24/08	11/01	10/04	25/01	22/02	30/11	07/09	21/03	21/12	■	28/09	01/01	04/04	28/12	08/02	03/08	09/11
Kettering Town	03/08	14/09	19/10	16/11	03/09	26/12	02/11	13/08	01/02	04/04	04/01	17/08	07/03	15/02	18/01	■	26/08	21/03	13/04	25/04	12/10	07/12
Kidderminster Harr.	21/03	31/08	14/09	04/01	07/12	03/09	04/04	24/08	18/04	08/02	12/10	09/11	13/08	29/02	26/12	10/04	■	26/10	03/08	30/11	18/01	22/02
King's Lynn Town	18/04	03/09	02/11	07/12	26/12	28/03	15/02	12/10	24/08	31/08	10/04	30/11	14/09	14/03	10/08	06/08	01/02	■	19/10	29/02	04/01	18/01
Leamington	10/04	12/10	04/01	31/08	28/03	06/08	29/02	18/01	10/08	09/11	14/09	26/10	26/12	30/11	03/09	24/08	14/03	08/02	■	22/02	07/12	18/04
Southport	24/08	10/04	03/09	14/09	18/01	12/10	01/02	26/12	06/08	18/04	28/03	14/03	07/12	10/08	19/10	31/08	07/03	16/11	02/11	■	15/02	04/01
Spennymoor Town	29/02	22/02	30/11	06/08	10/08	08/02	21/12	31/08	10/04	01/01	18/04	28/12	26/10	28/03	14/03	11/01	28/09	07/09	25/01	09/11	■	24/08
York City	11/01	30/11	14/03	28/03	19/10	10/08	01/01	01/02	29/02	21/12	06/08	26/08	25/04	28/12	15/02	25/01	02/11	28/09	17/08	07/09	13/04	■

Please note that the above fixtures may be subject to change.

National League South Fixtures 2019/2020 Season	Bath City	Billericay Town	Braintree Town	Chelmsford City	Chippenham Town	Concord Rangers	Dartford	Dorking Wanderers	Dulwich Hamlet	Eastbourne Borough	Hampton & Richmond Boro	Havant & Waterlooville	Hemel Hempstead Town	Hungerford Town	Maidstone United	Oxford City	Slough Town	St. Albans City	Tonbridge Angels	Wealdstone	Welling United	Weymouth
Bath City		04/01	03/08	18/04	26/12	09/11	30/11	26/10	22/02	14/09	03/09	04/04	18/01	13/08	12/10	26/08	10/04	08/02	17/08	07/12	21/03	07/03
Billericay Town	07/09		07/03	28/12	21/03	01/01	15/02	28/09	04/04	03/08	25/04	30/11	13/04	31/08	01/02	21/12	11/01	24/08	25/01	19/10	13/08	02/11
Braintree Town	29/02	06/08		01/01	18/04	28/12	10/04	26/08	07/09	17/08	30/11	21/12	15/02	02/11	19/10	28/09	25/01	14/03	11/01	10/08	04/04	01/02
Chelmsford City	31/08	02/09	26/12		14/09	07/03	12/08	09/11	26/10	18/01	03/08	25/04	04/01	07/12	13/04	16/11	22/02	28/03	08/02	12/10	24/08	21/03
Chippenham Town	01/01	10/08	31/08	21/12		11/01	01/02	28/12	28/09	28/03	13/04	25/01	19/10	25/04	15/02	06/08	16/11	29/02	07/09	14/03	02/11	24/08
Concord Rangers	15/02	26/12	03/09	06/08	12/10		14/09	16/11	25/04	07/12	04/01	01/02	02/11	19/10	24/08	29/02	10/08	13/04	14/03	28/03	31/08	18/01
Dartford	28/03	09/11	24/08	14/03	26/10	21/12		07/09	25/01	22/02	08/02	10/08	31/08	13/04	16/11	11/01	28/09	06/08	28/12	29/02	01/01	25/04
Dorking Wanderers	01/02	18/01	13/04	15/02	03/09	04/04	04/01		31/08	26/12	24/08	14/03	06/08	12/10	14/09	19/10	29/02	25/04	10/08	02/11	30/11	07/12
Dulwich Hamlet	02/11	16/11	04/01	01/02	18/01	17/08	07/12	18/04		10/04	26/12	19/10	14/03	14/09	03/09	28/03	26/08	10/08	29/02	06/08	15/02	12/10
Eastbourne Borough	21/12	29/02	25/04	28/09	30/11	25/01	02/11	01/01	24/08		31/08	13/04	01/02	04/04	14/03	10/08	07/09	11/01	06/08	15/02	28/12	19/10
Hampton & Rich.	28/12	17/08	28/03	29/02	26/08	07/09	19/10	10/04	01/01	18/04		06/08	10/08	01/02	02/11	14/03	21/12	25/01	28/09	16/11	11/01	15/02
Havant & Waterloo.	16/11	28/03	14/09	17/08	07/12	26/10	21/03	14/08	08/02	26/08	07/03		12/10	04/09	04/01	18/04	09/11	22/02	10/04	18/01	03/08	26/12
Hemel Hempstead T.	28/09	26/08	09/11	07/09	08/02	22/02	18/04	07/03	13/08	26/10	21/03	11/01		03/08	28/03	10/04	28/12	01/01	21/12	17/08	25/01	16/11
Hungerford Town	14/03	18/04	22/02	25/01	17/08	08/02	26/08	11/01	21/12	16/11	26/10	28/12	29/02		10/08	01/01	06/08	07/09	09/11	10/04	28/09	28/03
Maidstone United	11/01	26/10	08/02	26/08	09/11	10/04	04/04	21/12	28/12	13/08	22/02	07/09	30/11	21/03		25/01	17/08	28/09	01/01	18/04	07/03	03/08
Oxford City	13/04	14/09	18/01	04/04	07/03	03/08	12/10	08/02	30/11	21/03	13/08	31/08	24/08	26/12	07/12		26/10	09/11	22/02	04/01	25/04	03/09
Slough Town	24/08	12/10	07/12	02/11	04/04	21/03	18/01	03/08	13/04	04/01	14/09	15/02	03/09	07/03	25/04	01/02		31/08	30/11	26/12	19/10	13/08
St. Albans City	19/10	10/04	13/08	30/11	03/08	26/08	07/03	17/08	21/03	12/10	07/12	02/11	26/12	04/01	18/01	15/02	18/04		04/04	03/09	01/02	14/09
Tonbridge Angels	25/04	07/12	12/10	19/10	04/01	13/08	03/09	21/03	03/08	07/03	18/01	24/08	14/09	15/02	26/12	02/11	28/03	16/11		01/02	13/04	31/08
Wealdstone	25/01	08/02	21/03	11/01	13/08	30/11	03/08	22/02	07/03	09/11	04/04	28/09	25/04	24/08	31/08	07/09	01/01	28/12	26/10		21/12	13/04
Welling United	10/08	14/03	16/11	10/04	22/02	18/04	26/12	28/03	09/11	03/09	12/10	29/02	07/12	18/01	06/08	17/08	08/02	26/10	26/08	14/09		04/01
Weymouth	06/08	22/02	26/10	10/08	10/04	28/09	17/08	25/01	11/01	08/02	09/11	01/01	04/04	30/11	29/02	28/12	14/03	21/12	18/04	26/08	07/09	

Please note that the above fixtures may be subject to change.

Supporters' Guides and Tables books

Our Supporters' Guide series has been published since 1982 and the new 2020 editions contain the 2018/2019 Season's results and tables, Directions, Photographs, Telephone numbers, Parking information, Admission details, Disabled information and much more.

Our Football Tables books are perfect companions to the Supporters' Guides and contain historical Football League, Non-League and Scottish final tables up to the end of the 2018/2019 season.

THE SUPPORTERS' GUIDE TO PREMIER & FOOTBALL LEAGUE CLUBS 2020

This 36th edition covers all 92 Premiership and Football League clubs.   *Price £9.99*

NON-LEAGUE SUPPORTERS' GUIDE AND YEARBOOK 2020

This 28th edition covers all 68 clubs in Step 1 & Step 2 of Non-League football – the Vanarama National League, National League North and National League South.   *Price £9.99*

SCOTTISH FOOTBALL SUPPORTERS' GUIDE AND YEARBOOK 2020

The 27th edition featuring all Scottish Professional Football League, Highland League and Lowland League clubs.   *Price £9.99*

ENGLISH FOOTBALL LEAGUE & F.A. PREMIER LEAGUE TABLES 1888-2019

The 22nd edition contains every Football League & F.A. Premier League final table plus play-off results and F.A. Cup and League Cup semi-final & final results.   *Price £9.99*

NON-LEAGUE FOOTBALL TABLES 1889-2019

The 18th edition contains final league tables and historical notes for the 3 Leagues operating at Steps 3 and 4 of the pyramid, the Northern Premier League, Southern League and Isthmian League. This edition also contains tables for the Gloucestershire Northern Senior League 1922-1968.   *Price £9.99*

SCOTTISH FOOTBALL TABLES 1890-2019

The 9th edition contains final league tables for all Scottish Professional Football League, Scottish League, Scottish Premier League, Highland League and Lowland Football League seasons plus, for the first time, the East of Scotland Football League.   *Price £9.99*

These books are available UK & Surface post free from –

Soccer Books Limited (Dept. SBL)
72 St. Peter's Avenue
Cleethorpes, DN35 8HU
United Kingdom